It's Our Abbey

The People of Furness Abbey through the Years

Gill Jepson & Ron Creer

Furness Abbey Fellowship

Published in 2022 by Furness Abbey Fellowship

© Copyright Furness Abbey Fellowship

www.furnessabbeyfellowship.org

ISBN: 978-1-913898-35-9

Illustrations by Janet Pickering

Cover and Book interior Design by Russell Holden

www.pixeltweakspublications.com

FOREWORD

Seven hundred years ago
The Norman monks looked for a pleasant place
Where they might dwell; and their sagacious head,
Evanus, found a deep secluded dell,
Through which the silver singing ran;
Where grass was green and woods were plentiful,
And the strong hills were like God's sentinels
To guard from harm; and there, within the "Vale
Of Nightshade" found the monks a home.

When I first had the idea for this book, I had been looking for some specific information about "our Abbey". I have several books on it, all very scholarly but limited in scope, concentrating on the history up to dissolution and the architecture of the building – those by Alice Leach in particular are important. But I wanted something easy to read and more about the people who lived or worked or visited the abbey, so I searched online and sadly found the same academic works. There are, of course, a couple of books for children about monks and abbeys that mention Furness briefly but only in passing. In addition there are some local fiction books that were inspired by the abbey, especially the "Out of Time" series for adolescents. I looked in the abbey shop and on the English Heritage online store but again was disappointed.

I envisaged a book about "the people who were there": the monks, the local farmers and gentry, the masons who built it, the abbots in charge of it, the soldiers who despoiled it, the men who built the railway that passed by it, the famous people who visited it, children who played in its grounds and local people who go frequently because they love it so much. I was certain such a book would appeal to visitors who wanted an easy-to-read introduction to our Abbey and its people.

However, I also wanted the book to be a mix of imagination – how did these folk feel while there – and historical accuracy for names and dates, etc. I could create the former but needed help with the latter. I did not hesitate: there was only one person I could turn to, the person born and bred near the abbey, the one who has written about it many times [including her books mentioned earlier, the "Out of Time" series], the one who has taken many guided tours of the abbey and works for English Heritage there. Moreover, in one way she was my boss! **Gill Jepson** knows more about the abbey than anyone I know and, even in the several local history books she has written for Amberley Press, ensures the abbey is included in each! Gill is also the founder and Chair of Furness Abbey Fellowship, the small charity that supports EH in its work at the abbey by publicising it, running events there [especially the Medieval Fair each September] and raises its profile whenever possible. Since I am the vice-chair of FAF and Gill is a friend, I asked her to write the book with me. She was enthusiastic and very supportive and did not hesitate to agree. I showed her my plan and we decided to share chapters, proof-read each other's and get on with it. She has been the fount of factual knowledge for me and I am very grateful that she agreed to co-write the book.

To complete the creativity process, **Janet Pickering** has added her wonderful drawings to illustrate chapters where photographs are not available.

I hope you enjoy it, learn something from it and, most of all, come to visit Our Abbey and see for yourself the "gem of Furness".

Ron Creer

INTRODUCTION

From its founding in 1127 by a group of Savigniac monks from Normandy, the Abbey of St Mary of Furness grew to be the second most powerful abbey in the north of England. It changed to be a Cistercian house a short time after its inception while still being developed as a building.

Early on Furness had already established 'daughter houses' in Cumbria and The Isle of Man. Under the Cistercians two further houses were established in Ireland. For 400 years Furness Abbey enjoyed substantial wealth based on farming, the wool trade and control of natural mineral resources. It became the predominant landowner in Low Furness and the Furness Fells and controller of the natural, deep water harbour at Piel. Cistercian monks, or 'White Monks' as they were known because of their undyed habits, had a reputation for austerity and seclusion from secular life. Much of the hard, physical work of the abbey was undertaken by lay brothers whilst the choir monks devoted their time to daily services, prayer, meditation, reading and study. At the time of its dissolution by Henry VIII, Furness was the second richest Cistercian monastery in England after Fountains. The deed of surrender was signed by the abbot, the prior and monks on 9th April 1537. It is known that lead was stripped from the roofs, the tracery of windows broken and buildings dismantled while the monks were still in residence.

For more than 200 years afterwards, ownership changed hands many times until finally coming to the Cavendish family who still own the land today. During the late 18th and early 19th centuries the ruins became an essential place to visit for poets, artists, antiquarians and travellers. J M W Turner was drawn here to paint and William Wordsworth loved the place from his boyhood days. His Guide To The Lakes did much to make the abbey a tourist attraction. The opening of the Furness Railway in 1846 and the Furness Abbey Hotel soon after put Furness Abbey firmly on the Victorian tourist trail.

In the twentieth century it has been visited by thousands who came to love its tranquil setting and it has been used as a setting for all sorts of purposes from Mystery Plays to wedding photos.

With all this history in mind, let us now turn to learn about the people who inhabited or visited the abbey for a range of reasons and discover what they thought of this "jewel in the crown of Furness".

And, if you have not yet visited "our abbey" we urge you to do so and see why so many people love it so much.

Gill Jepson

Contents

CHAPTER 1

EUDO DE SURDEVAL 1124-7

I am so excited. Today we finally reached our new home where we hope to settle and set up a new monastic life, God willing. It has been quite a journey but we are at our final destination.

My name is Eudo de Surdeval and I am one of the twelve brothers from our base in Savigny in France who were invited by Count Stephen of Boulogne to set up a new monastery in England. Although I will miss my fellow countrymen back in Normandy, I know that God has called me to work with new people in northern England so that is what I must do. I am fortunate to be under the guidance of Abbot Ewan d'Avranches, a godly and dedicated man, who has led us here and will be in charge of setting up the new Abbey.

The journey was long and tiring as our horses could take us no more than forty miles a day with their load of holy books and relics but we were content to bear this travail in doing such sacred work. After a night in lodgings at the port of Harfleur, we crossed the sea and landed in England at Hastings, staying the first night in our new country at Battle Abbey where the local monks, though Benedictines and so not of our order, were happy to accommodate us. I found it odd to be staying on the site of the great battle nearly sixty years ago where Duke William of Normandy defeated the English to become the first French king of England. That did mean that we had few language problems, at least while in the south of the country, for he had helped our tongue to spread in their lands.

Our journey from there was, of necessity, not direct as we needed to ensure we had holy lodgings each night. Thus, we rode to Canterbury and stayed once more with Benedictine brothers in the great cathedral there. I must confess to having mixed feelings about these huge cathedrals; I know they are built to the glory of God but does He really want such elaborate and ornate structures as this is planned to be, I wonder. Naturally, I kept these thoughts to myself.

From Canterbury we travelled to London and stayed at Westminster Abbey, then onto Ely, Peterborough, Burton [we were getting used to Benedictine ways by now!], Tutbury and the last long journey to the Amounderness[1] where we were supposed to live in lands granted to us by our lord Stephen.

On July 4th in the year of our Lord 1124 we arrived at Tulket for the lands allotted to us for the lands next to this place. In some ways the land was suitable: it was not far from the town of Prestoune[2], had plenty of woodland that could supply our needs and had the protection of the castle. We set up our base on the flat lands immediately beneath the hill on which the castle stood and started to build our abbey. For three years we worked so hard on it with the determination and dedication Abbot Ewan demanded of us. But somehow it seems God was telling us this was not the right place as we could not get the foundations secure in the marshy ground all around there. Streams, springs and wells were all about us – indications of the wetness of the land. In the spring of 1127 the Abbot called us together in what was to become the chapter house and discussed the problem. He informed us that we had also been allocated some land further north, in the land called Fournes[3] or the Manor of Hugun[4] and, from what he had heard, this may be more suitable for an abbey. From the discussion it was clear that we had little choice although I felt disappointed that we had wasted three years on this unsuitable site and, to be honest, that we were to go further north where it may be even colder.

It took quite a few weeks to organise matters at Tulket, gather our belongings together and prepare for another journey north. So, it was early July in 1127 that we set off for what was to become the final journey for me and most of my brethren. This journey was not simple as the "sands" mentioned before were in fact a huge bay with fast flowing tides and unreliable sands. We reached its edge at a tiny village called Slyne where, fortunately, a local man who knew the tides, guided us across the bay. I was in wonder at his knowledge and the zig-zag path he took in order, he said, to avoid some dangerous channels en route. In some ways the bay reminded me of the Norman coast with its sweeping sands, but this was not a beach next to a sea but a much vaster area of sand covered by water for only briefly twice a day. I felt the majesty of Creation as we crossed.

---

1 The old name for this part of Lancashire
2 Preston, like many place names at the time, had no fixed spelling and you will find many such differences from modern spellings in this book.
3 Furness today of course
4 Another old name for Furness

Eudo de Surdeval

We landed near a village called Ceartmel[5], then travelled across a hilly peninsula to another part of the bay where another guide took us over more sands till we reached the land of Fourness. It was but a short walk south west from here to our final destination. Our new home was in a valley, the Vale of Beckangs Ghyll[6] near the town of Daltoune[7].

My first site of the vale took my breath away – it was beautiful. A curved sweep of a valley with woods, flowers, hills and the nearness of the sea – all was wondrous. And the site seemed very suitable for the building of an abbey. Nearby were places where we could quarry for stone – it was lovely red sandstone in this area, perfect for carving – and fields also where we could have farms to grow produce for our needs.

The abbot gathered us together in the vale and we prayed to God to thank Him for our safe arrival and ask for blessing on the building we will create here. It is to be dedicated to Our Lady and called St Mary's of Fournes. Amen to that.

* * * *

And so the next months and years will be spent quarrying the stone, planning our new building and creating a proper community. I know Abbot Ewan has the skills to get this done. I am looking forward to it all, praise God.

---

5   Cartmel
6   Now spelled Beckansgill
7   Dalton-in-Furness

CHAPTER 2

EWAN D'AVRANCHES
The Abbaye De Fournes 1127

We have recovered from our arduous journey from Tulketh for a more favourable destination in a backwater named Beckangs Ghyll. We have been granted not only land, but the vast forest and demesne of Fournes (Furness), small islands including that of Hougenai which local peasants name Wonay or Walney, the manor of Ulver's ton excepting land of Michael le Fleming. We have retained our fisheries on the great Lune near Lancaster and we will be able to negotiate land to benefit the abbey I am certain.

I felt some trepidation as we travelled across treacherous sands and wild moors, with even wilder inhabitants in the mean villages along the way. In fact, this place resides almost as an island, with shifting sands, great estuaries, and limited land routes. But here we found a veritable paradise of rich land, abundant forests, crystal streams and stone with which to build barely concealed beneath the ground. Indeed, this valley is full of the riches of the earth, granted to us by God himself.

The younger brothers are energised by this new home and are clearly inspired to do God's Work, but they must be patient, for this will not be an easy task. I, the first abbot of Fournes, Ewan d'Avranches, must prepare and plan carefully to ensure our efforts glorify the Lord and that we harness the gifts we have been given for our endeavours.

Our first task should be to begin the building of the church, but this must wait for the masons to arrive from Normandy. The people here are ignorant of the skills needed to build a great church alone, so we must bring skilled craftsmen from our beloved homeland. We are fortunate that my Lord Stephen had foresight and despatched a man to oversee the building of temporary wooden lodgings and a small chapel for our immediate use.

EWAN D'AVRANCHES

The trees in the valley have been somewhat cleared and we have discovered a small spring in addition to the two streams which enter the valley. The vale is sheltered and protected by high banks on each side; we have already seen some fine red sandstone outcrops to the south and I am sure this will be most suitable for the construction.

This day I rode out with the prior to survey the land. We rode down towards the sea and passed through a salt marsh with an abundance of reeds. We will make good use of these for thatch and strewing on the floor of our rooms. 'Tis not too far from the abbey and we will be able to bring reeds quite easily. We saw that there were ponds of brackish water, which gave us the thought that we can make our own salt pans and perchance create a salt house. This will be a great resource and we might even trade this to other places.

We discovered a natural harbour at Barrai,[8] an insignificant hamlet of peasants living from the land and sea. Fishing will be important to us and we must learn to exploit these fine resources for our benefit. A poor boatman took us across the narrow channel to another small isle, which was good agricultural land and had few inhabitants. A second larger isle we discovered to be Waney[9] had small settlements of cottagers who live a rough existence, having little in the way of comfort. There is good fishing here and arable land to work. There were many coneys[10] and hares racing across the land and would make a goodly place for a warren. However, there is great hardship from the winter tides and we must work to create dykes and ditches to help reduce the damage. The peasants look strong and able to undertake this task as boon[11] work.

There are several islets which methinks can be useful too. One larger isle, the Pile of Fouldray[12] lends itself to fortification and would make a goodly lookout for invasion by pirates or the barbarian Scots. This land is full of surprises and will no doubt make our abbey formidable and an appropriate monument to the glory of the Lord God.

---

8   Barrow-in-Furness
9   Walney
10 Rabbits
11 Boon work was work peasants had to give freely to their manorial lord (In this case the abbey) on
    certain occasions-such as the lord's harvest
12 Piel Island

The roads are dangerous and few. This will be a hazard at first, but no doubt as we grow in size, we can set our minds to this as well. Our monks are few in number, but we will be drawing novices from the noble families about[13]. It will bring strength to us and we will manage our lands with more efficiency. I pray we can gain some of the peasants to take holy orders and work our lands as lay brothers. They will benefit as well as the abbey and God. These are hopes to be fulfilled in time; we must first continue our prayers and ensure that the abbey church is built.

Yesterday, I was pleased to welcome a lord from Kircheby[14] who wishes to give us land and gifts in return for masses to be said for his soul on his death. He promises his youngest son as a novice when he reaches seven, which is the beginning for our new community and heralds its growth and prosperity.

My own twelve brothers will set the standard for the congregation; they each have their own strengths and I see great potential in Brother Eudo, who is sober and straightforward in his beliefs and is a of good Norman stock. I await with anticipation the arrival of the master mason and his journeymen, for they will make our dream of an abbey a reality. In the meantime, I must content myself with arranging our stores for winter; we had to collect supplies from the local peasants and ensure our vegetables were planted. We are building a flock of the rugged sheep from these lands and have goats and a few cattle. This will be hard work until we are properly established. And always I must be careful not to become too proud, 'tis a sin.

I shall cease these musings, for I must prepare for vespers as the night is drawing close. I will give thanks today for the revelation of the profusion of wealth this new land offers, and I welcome the chance to complete my *opus dei* in this blessed place. Deo gratias.

---

13 It was common for wealthy families to send their youngest sons to be monks if there was not enough land for them.
14 Kirkby-in-Furness

CHAPTER 3

LOUIS DE LISON
Master Mason 1150

I did not want to come and at first I resisted. I, a Master Mason, renowned throughout the land of the Normans as the best stone mason available, was more than happy to spend my working days on the many projects here in France where I was appreciated and well paid. So, to be summonsed to travel to England to work was not an attractive proposition. England? *Mon Dieu*, the place was supposed to be uncivilised and without the sophistication I was used to here in my homeland.

But the pay the abbot of the new abbey offered was good [these monasteries do seem to have funds for anything at all] and I was allowed to bring across my own team. Also the new abbey they wanted built was going to be grand, they said, and my pride sparked me to accept.

When I first arrived in Fournes, I confess to being very pleasantly surprised, not only on a professional basis in the level site and plentiful supply of water and excellent local red sandstone which was idea for building, but also in the beauty of the area. The woods especially are very attractive as well as supplying us with the necessary timber.

I mentioned my team. They included my free mason specialists, such as the stonecutters who would be responsible for most of the skilled stone work – shaping it for doors, windows, joints, etc. Most were my apprentices and so have learned many of the skills I passed on. They were good at their work and I trusted them … although I still checked their work afterwards for it's my reputation at stake, *n'est-ce pas*? Others knew all about wood and its uses, for example. These men would also be the ones to construct the scaffolding and cranes which were needed to take the stones to the higher positions. Then there were the rough masons who chisel the blocks as well as laying the exterior stone; a couple were the apprentices I had in France but still raw and not yet ready for the more skilled tasks. Finally were the quarrymen and labourers, but most of these were local hired by the abbot to cut the rock using iron-headed pickaxes to make grooves which were then deepened with chisels and wedges to split it. Others would haul the stone on stretchers or sledges driven by oxen, fit it in place with ropes on a winding wheel and cut.

LOUIS DE LISON

Even more would lay timber – we had to teach some which trees were oak, the only timber I would accept for the building, though other trees were fine for the scaffolding. They also learned how to mix the lime, sand and horsehair which we used to cement the stones together.

Our first job was to build my lodge, my base where I lived and worked on the plans. *Naturellement*, I consulted the abbot as to what he required, but mostly to offer him choices, although he was content to leave details to me. I was well aware of what church layout was as well as the need for a chapter house, accommodation, etc. Most days I could be found on my hands and knees, the paper plans on the floor, designing precisely what would go where, but occasionally I would spend time in the natural dip that appears like an amphitheatre just adjacent to where we were building the abbey, for this was where we brought the stone and timber before using it. My lads would search through looking for the best piece for each location and at times I would take a break from my designing and wander off to advise.

My resistance to working in England gradually dissipated as my work continued. I was kept very busy but I grew to love it, and the results it was producing. The abbot was supportive and, after agreeing to my plans, he left me to get on with it, just checking on occasion that I had everything I needed. My team increased in number over the years, sometimes by more masons from Normandie and at times by local men who had skills we needed such as carpentry for the timbers or plumbing for the water courses. I was especially proud of one local man who turned out to have hidden skills and a natural talent for working with stone. His name was Ned Thompson and I took him on as an apprentice until, after some years, he became the first English free mason in the region.

As years passed, it became clear that this was probably going to be my last piece of work. I was in my late 40s when we arrived in Fournes and building an abbey on this scale would take a good twenty years, if not more. In addition there were times when we had to pause, occasionally for months, while the abbot secured funds for us to continue. It's a good job he had lands, farms and local benefactors to support him. But, if this was to be my last creation I wanted my legacy to be a great one. Fournes Abbey would be a building *magnifique*.

In fact, it did take more than twenty years, but, by the year of our Lord 1147, my plans were nearing completion. The nave, quire, transept and presbytery were finished and internally kept in the simple fashion demanded by the monks. I was secretly proud of my building and delighted that my mark was on it. Indeed, each of my free masons left their mark on the part of the building they constructed, usually on the upper stones and we truly believed that they would remain there for many centuries as evidence of the men who built the abbey. The carvings of figures too were individual glories, sometimes of the monks who had annoyed us, sometimes of ourselves. We normally added both marks and carvings on higher stones where few people would see them but some were more clearly visible.

****

Now, nearing seventy years of age and not able to move as freely as I once did (those years on my hands and knees had taken their toll), I was thinking of retiring and returning to France when an event decided things for me. Pope Eugenius ordered that the Savigny order was to be disbanded and merged into the great Cistercian Order in order to stop some of the laxity shown by monks in many monasteries. In Fournes this created much argument and bad feeling where the older monks who had found ways of personally benefitting from their work were very unhappy. The bitterness affected our everyday life and even we masons felt it was no longer a happy place to work. Moreover, the Cistercians demanded some changes to the fabric of the building which went against some of my designs: they believed in greater simplicity, whitewashed walls and stark interiors. I felt my ideas were of the past and it was time for me to go home. So it's back to Normandy for me. God be with ye, Abbey church of Saint Mary. Bon chance.

CHAPTER 4

WIMUND
The Rebellious Monk

*AS TOLD BY GUILELMUS NEUBRIGENSIS
(WILLIAM OF NEWBURGH) ABOUT 1170*

From *Historia rerum Anglicarum* ("History of English Affairs")

As a chronicler of some import I encounter many people whose story must be told to add to the knowledge we have of the years past. One such of these is the notorious Wimund who I have had discourse with on many occasions at the abbey of Byland where he now whiles away his days, aged, blind and impotent.

He was of lowly birth, most agree, but because of his dissembling and lies 'tis challenging to discover the real truth of his origins. It is known that he was born in a most obscure spot in England[15], not too distant from the great abbey of St Mary of Fournes. Indeed, this holy abbey did give him succour and shelter in his youth and time of greatest need. By the charity of the monks Wimund was given an education befitting a youth of less obscure birth and he was a willing and able scholar, with a sharp mind and retentive memory. His ardent temper and competent eloquence[16] ensured his position in the abbey and marked him out as a young man of prospect. The abbot entrusted much in him and he was one of the party of monks despatched from Fournes to the wild Isle of Mann in the year of our Lord 1134, only seven years hence from the foundation of the mother house. The monks' task was to found a daughter house at Rushen, at the behest of Amlaib mac Gofraid, Lord King of the Isles, to civilise and educate this wild land.

---

15 This description is from William's own text
16 A quote by William of Wimund's character

13

This new community of monks was much celebrated by the people and Wimund, young as he was, became well versed in winning acclaim and support. His tall and robust build, his fair countenance and sweetness of address did cleave him to the common folk and he won great honours from the King of Mann. His noble and learned appearance did persuade the people to elect him to be their bishop and this was not opposed by the Lord Thurstan who was lately Archbishop of York. In time this power, as is oft the case, did inspire a hunger for greater power still and 'twas then Wimund issued forth the claim that he was the son of the Mormaer of Moray[17], cheated of his inheritance by David King of the Scots. Those who supported his claim cited the charity and care of the monks of Fournes for him as proof of his origin and his preferment by the King of Mann; 'tis a matter which has scant credence.

His arrogance and greed for power knew no bounds and his pride led him to rise even higher than his episcopal offices would allow. His bishopric had its seat upon the Isle of Skye and he continued to feign himself heir to the Moray earldom. He fell into swift conflict with the Bishop of Whithorn, Gille Aidan, who had been endowed during Wimund's episcopate. Wimund feared his bishopric being partitioned in favour of his rival and determined to oppose this at all costs. His haughty speaking mouth and proud heart[18] led him to attempt taking back not only his inheritance from the Scottish King David, exacting cruel revenge upon the Scots, but removing all threats from Gille Aidan. His fiery rhetoric drew many to him and his warrior band grew in number; making him reckless and fierce. Indeed, this "Fisher of men"[19] soon changed to an unscrupulous hunter of men, akin to "Nimrod"[20] wasting all before him with rapine and slaughter.[21]

Wimund was sly and took to the seas and forests to hide until his rapacious raids began again. The Scots were hard pressed to stop this reign of terror and destruction and could no more catch him than a slippery eel. His audacity knew no limit but he sealed his fate upon demanding tribute from the Scottish bishop, who denied his right to do so. The bishop did gather liegemen and men at arms to him and took battle to Wimund in the hope that he would be suppressed. And God was on his side, even being the smaller force, the bishop struck true with his hand axe, dealing a hard blow at the start of battle. Wimund fell instantly to the ground. The bishop's small militia was emboldened by this sign from the

---

17 Mormaer is Gaelic for Earl
18 Taken from a quote by William de Newburgh
19 Biblical reference to Jesus' disciples who he charged with being "fishers of men"
20 Nimrod was the great grandson of Noah and is mentioned in Genesis as a great hunter
21 William de Newburgh's words

Almighty, and much blood was spilt, many of Wimund's band killed and driven hence. Wimund fled and went to ground like a fox to his lair, until his wounds did heal, but this did not cause him to cease his wicked ravaging of the coast.

King David of the Scots took it upon himself to finally defeat this proud enemy, not by battle but by wily means. He made pretence that he believed Wimund's rash claims of nobility and indeed, he granted Fournes and another province to him. The knave Wimund, in good faith did make a tour and visitation of his lands, as grand as any Lord, surveying his fiefdom. 'Twas then, when he was most haughty and triumphant, that a number of enemies who were unable to endure either his power or his insolence[22] did set upon him and brought him down. His penance was harsh as befitted his behaviour "unbecoming as it was to a bishop" and they bound and held him, did put out his eyes for both were wicked. They then set to and made him a eunuch for the sake of the kingdom of Scotland and to provide 'gainst further excess. He was removed to the abbey of Byland, a daughter house of Fournes, there within to spend the rest of his lyfe.

I have misfortuned to hear the impertinence of this wily, old villain when I saw him at the abbey of Byland on divers occasions. He doth gleefully recount the terrible details of his irreverent lyfe with no glimpse of shame or penitence. The physical pains and punishment he has endured have done nought to stem his wicked arrogance and his soul will be in peril until he repent. Indeed, he doth boast that no man hath brought him down, and that God alone was able to vanquish him by the faith of a simple bishop[23]. He is unrepentant and castigates those enemies who did blind and neuter him. He sayeth e'en had he the eye of a sparrow, his enemies should have little occasion to rejoice at what they did to him.

Wimund will undoubtedly be cast into the pit and will regret his evil ways. On hearing of most audacious acts as well as his merited misfortunes this can be the only fate for this wicked knave. Such things ought not to be passed over in silence, that posterity may learn how he who resisteth the proud, but giveth grace to the humble was illustrated by this individual.[24]

_____

22 William of Newburgh's words
23 Referring to the axe blow by the Scottish bishop
24 From the Historie of William de Newburgh TR. J Stevenson (Llanerch facsimile, Felinfach, 1996)

POSTSCRIPT

The scandalous tale of Wimund has to be looked at from a distance and therefore today we probably do not understand the whole story. William of Newburgh was a chronicler and canon from the Augustinian order, observing from a distant position too. Although he had met Wimund in his later years, he has no direct knowledge of the truth of the story. He is somewhat judgmental and dismisses Wimund's claim out of hand, preferring to demonise him as a piratical bishop. However, it was not unusual for bishops and abbots to command a militia in time of conflict, particularly during this period when England was engaged in the "Anarchy" a civil war between factions for the crown. Furness would have been in Stephen's camp as he had endowed the abbey. Wimund was apparently born at the time of the abbey's establishment and had been taken in or educated by them. By the time he left for Rushen the Anarchy was underway and as is suggested by the name, life would have been quite dangerous and unruly.

William ignores some of the more interesting observations which would seem to support Wimund's claim to noble birth. One particular point is that the claim was not denied by the Mormaer of Moray even though he was alive during the first seven years of Wimund's rise to power as a bishop. Neither he, nor the King of Scotland, intervened with this elevation, which might suggest there was truth in the claim.

Byland Abbey - last residence of Wimund

The trouble started when Wimund began to make challenges to the rival bishop Gille Aidan, the power struggle then presented a risk to land ownership and the Scottish crown. The rebellious Wimund fought on, leaving what would have been a reasonably comfortable position as Bishop of the Isles, which as someone of low birth he might have valued and accepted as a lifetime achievement, but as a displaced noble would perhaps emphasise that he was due much more.

William does not accept any possibility of the claim being true at all.

Wimund's ancestry has been suggested by some to be linked more closely to the Scottish throne-being the illegitimate issue of Oengus of Moray who was grandson of King Lulach (Macbeth's stepson) and who died in 1130. This would give weight to why The King of Scots eventually suppressed Wimund, because he was a potential pretender to his throne.

However, considering the close link to Cumbria and his education at Furness Abbey it seems more convincing that he was a bastard child of William Fitz Duncan, the later Mormaer of Moray. The illegitimate son of a nobleman could have easily been sent to an abbey to be raised, at the cost of his father. This level of influence would also have marked him for great things in the future and would have placed him in prime position for a meteoric rise. Of course we will never know the truth as the evidence we have is cursory and the main source is William. William would have brought his own prejudice to the story, disliking any facts which gave authenticity to the birth-right and challenging what he would see as the natural course of events and rank. As limited as the evidence is, the story has endured and William's account was allegedly taken from speaking with Wimund himself, so it is up to us to define the facts as best we can.

CHAPTER 5

ABBOT JOHN COCKERHAM 1327

I have this day been granted permission by our sovereign lord, King Edward[25] to crenellate my dwelling house at Fotheray[26] and build a defence against the perilous Scots. 'Tis hoped that this and the new fortification of Daltoun will give some security for our lands. We do still feel the scourge of the attacks in 1316 and then in the Great Raid of 1322 led by Robert de Brus[27]. Indeed, our parishes are impoverished and can barely scrape together enough money to send to his Holiness the Pope in Rome. Our "Peter's Pence", as it is called, is much reduced and there is nought to be done!

I well remember the day the Scottish devils began their invasion of the lands in the west. They devastated the abbey of Holmcultram e'en though it had great ties with the Scots, and Bruce's father lays at rest there. There is no deterring these vile heathens and their murderous ways. They swept through the countryside, destroying everything in their path, stealing and pillaging along the way. We could see the black smoke from the destruction from miles away and we knew they were close by our Manor of Low Furness. I made the decision to ride out with my trusted prior, the cellarer and two men at arms from Daltoun for protection, to meet Robert the Bruce to persuade him to cease his evil venture.

I knew we were in God's care but was uneasy nevertheless, for we had heard of the wily nature of this man. We met outside the town and I believe we caught him unawares. He was surprised that a man of God would face him like this. His men bristled with weapons and looked like demons from the abyss, with their wild eyes, unkempt hair, and bloody apparel. It struck terror into our hearts, but we had the advantage of surprise. We led Bruce and his personal guard to the Courthouse; there we sat, civilised around an oaken table, and shared a light repast with ale and parleyed for hours.

---

25 King Edward ll ruled 1307-27
26 Pile of Fouldray or Piel Island
27 Robert the Bruce

Abbot John Cockerham

We finally reached terms which would benefit our manor and the people therein. 'Twas not easy and neither was it without some harm, but at least we had prevented more land and property being razed to the ground.

The Bruce was content with the deal, which gave him sufficient booty to take with him. As a matter of expediency, he was invited to spend the night in comfort in my lodgings at the abbey. His rough men camped on the moor at Mouzel and his guards were lodged in the guest house by the hospitaller. They were a rowdy bunch, carousing and drinking into the night and fighting amongst themselves like barnyard animals. The hospitaller was more than once called to bang heads together - luckily, he is a broad backed young fellow.

Lord Robert was a milder man than I expected. His intelligence shone from him and he had a decided strategy in these raids, with much support from his countrymen against our sovereign lord Edward. Bruce claims overlordship of the lands in the north and had even been crowned by his fellow men in 1306. His ambition and audacity knows no bounds and he intends to rout the English from his land forever.

He is an educated man, and we had a pretty discourse on religion and politics beside my generous fire, oiled for conversation with good Gascon wine. He swore on the cross that he would destroy no more of our abbey lands but would repair back to Scotland in peace. On the morrow we bade him goodbye and he set off laden with gold and produce, herding some of our finest sheep and cattle before him.

We heard in the following days that he had left our Manor without further damage; but his wicked hordes laid waste to Cartmel, crossing the sands of the bay to then run amok in Lancaster. One thing is certain we will ne'er forget the visitation and will be forced to pay for it for many a year. Henceforth we must be more prepared and by the goodness of the King we can remedy our defences. The peasants will continue to struggle to pay their tithes to the abbey and even feed themselves, because of the crops and livestock which were appropriated or destroyed by our enemy. Our Almoner will be busy if we are to prevent a famine and the disease which always follows. We must pray for better days ahead and for the good welfare of our people. Of course, we must remember those who died unshriven in these raids and for the souls of those poor persons who were taken prisoner. But most keenly, we must pray for continued peace.

Da, Domine, propitious pacem in diebus nostis, ut, ope misericordiae tuae aduiti, et a peccato simus semper liberi et ab omni perturbiatone secure. Per Christum Dominum nostrum. Amen.[28]

---

28 Graciously give peace oh Lord, in our days, that, being assisted by the help of Thy mercy, we may
    ever be free from sin and safe from all disturbance. Through Christ our Lord. Amen.

CHAPTER 6

BROTHER NORMAN 1350

I love my life. I am always grateful to God for being able to do His will this way. I may not be clever enough to be a scholar like the "monachi"[29], but I am content to serve the Lord by other means as a lay monk.

Because I had been brought up on a farm, I was used by the abbot as a "conversi"[30], and sent to work at the various granges the abbey owned both in Lancashire North of the Sands and in Westmoreland. At first I worked especially with the sheep on the hill farms around Conistone and Cartmel for wool was a very lucrative crop for the abbey and the tenant farmers needed both help and monitoring. In the times since the Black Death[31] in particular, they had fewer hands to help on the farms.

Most of the farmers were hardworking and honest, and I enjoyed helping them for it reminded me of my youth when I too worked in similar sloping fields further north in Cumberland. In particular I loved lambing time in spring for bringing new life into the world was a blessing from God. Mind you, the local breed, the Herdwick, need little human assistance mostly as the yows[32] are good mothers and extremely hardy. But sometimes they needed a helping hand if a birth was not straightforward. I did other work too, of course, - I was becoming skilled [Lord, forgive my pride] at shearing too – and I lived among the farm labourers and felt very much I was one of them; I hope they felt the same about me, although there were mutterings about the time I spent in prayer during the day.

Once I saw that all was well on one grange and the tenant was working effectively for us, I would move on to another and help there for a time.

---

29 Choir monks who can read and write
30 Lay monks who worked away from the abbey doing mostly manual work
31 The Black Death of 1346-53 killed about 40% of the population
32 Ewes – the term "yow" is still in use locally today

We lay brothers have much freedom as the abbot trusted us but the chamberlain would still check the rents and know if any of our granges were not paying their dues. This did happen at times when farming fell on hard times, especially if the farmer was new or lazy. Only once did we [I say we, although I, of course, had nothing to do with it] have to eject a tenant farmer from the grange for not paying his rent, and he was very lazy indeed and I heard a rumour that he was even selling some produce elsewhere when we had the agreement to buy all his produce.

Another task I was given one year was less suited to my experience [and talents] and that was fishing. This was not something I had done before but I always do as I am told and so I joined another lay monk, Brother Stephen, who was an experienced fisherman. He had a boat he used on Conistone Water, catching fish called char. The equipment he used seemed complex to me and I did try to do as he said and look out for lines moving to indicate a fish was caught. But often my concentration was not constant and my attention distracted by the beauty of God's creation all around me. Stephen's chastisement did provoke improved concentration from me and gradually I got better at this task.

One job I really liked was accompanying the produce, whether from farms or fisheries, back to our abbey. I was not always the chosen one for this task but when I was I looked forward to being back in our spiritual home. I did miss the abbey whilst away: it is in such a tranquil location and the building soothes my soul like nowhere else. I hope it will always do this for people for many years to come.

While back at the abbey my space in the dorter[33] was sufficient for my needs but I have never understood why we were kept so far apart from the choir monks, even having to eat in a separate frater area. Truth be told, the "monachi" did treat us with what has to be called contempt at times, their spotless white habits looking so clean and superior to our old brown ones which were usually spattered with dirt from the fields, and their life of devotion seen as of a higher calling than our manual work ... I suppose in truth it was but they did make it obvious that they looked down upon us. To be honest – and I hope this is not a blasphemous thought – I preferred the company of farming folk to those of my brothers at the abbey. Indeed, my vows of poverty especially were, I believe, kept to more than many of the choir monks in the Vale of Beckansgill. While their numbers seem to have swollen I am saddened to hear how the number of us lay monks has dropped in recent years.

---

33 Dormitory

So, while at the abbey, which was never for more than a few days, I kept to myself or with other lay monks. I learned from them about other tasks we were set, some brewing beer, some tanning leather, some milling corn. All brought wealth to our Cistercian order, wealth which troubled me as we were an order devoted to poverty.

I learned that we lay monks were scattered over such a large area, from the Yorkist lands to the east to even the Isle of Mann far out in the west where the abbey of Rushen was our base – but my fear of boats meant I was relieved I never went across the Irish Sea to Mann. Brother Joseph, however, seemed to enjoy his life across there, as he told me one day after we finished our meal together in the parlour.

Tomorrow I return to the granges, this time towards Cartmel, and I am not sad to be going. Hard labour is not a problem for me and I am happy to serve the Lord among animals and crops. Farewell, dear Furness Abbey.

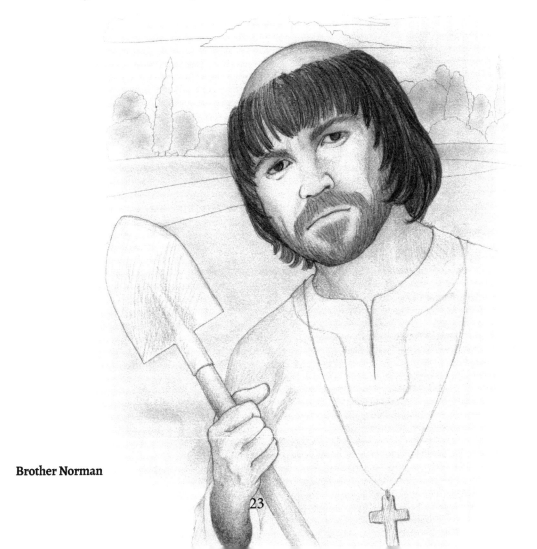

Brother Norman

CHAPTER 7

BROTHER JOHN STELL
Abbey Scribe 1412

One final letter and I am finished for the day. The light has been poor today and I have had to light my small cresset lamp. This new Scriptorium is a small room with high windows, 'tis warm being next to the calefactory[34], but gloomier than the cloister alley which on a good day is bathed in sunlight. My poor hands function better in this warm place, but my eyes strain to see well. These restrictions help me to appreciate my work and make it more worthwhile through the suffering I endure. The cloister is a beautiful quadrangle, edged by low walls and open windows with decorative tracery, but the paved floor and windows can be cold in inclement weather, making my fingers cramp and ache.

I do love working in the cloister in summer, the smell of the herbs from the garth is heady and the hum of the insects and bees around the apple trees allow me to revel in God's good work. The warmth of the sun eases the bones, and repairs the pain caused by the hunching over the parchment, the ink flows freely, and all is relaxed. My carrell is just the correct height and the wooden slope allows me a good view of my script; up to twelve brethren can work here protected by the vaulting in the sloped roof and the wall behind.

I have been given a great work to create by Abbot John of Daltune, a studious man who appreciated my illuminations. He intends to compile all abbey charters, land grants and a "historie" of our abbey and has given me the task because of my fine drawing. He did, however, warn me that I must improve my copying and accuracy. I know this is my weakness, I can spend much time on a beautiful picture of Our Lady and the Saints but take less care in copying dry documents often poorly written years ago.

---

34 Warming room-heated with a fire

We have a goodly library with two great book cupboards next to the Chapter House; these are full of the documents I needs must copy. I much prefer designing and decorating the letters and panels in my work and I admit I take some pride in this. I am oft reminded by the Abbot of the words of St Benedict[35] who tells us "if there be skilled workmen in the monastery, let them work at their art in all humility"; he believes I take too much pride in my craft.

These Coucher[36] Books, as they are named, will take many years to complete and will present a useful catalogue of all our abbey business when finished. I pray by the grace of God I will live long enough to see them finished; I would not like to think of them being taken on by another scribe as my work would become forgotten.

I must confess to something now: I wonder if the good Abbot will notice my misdemeanour? I pray he will not. I was so involved with my decorations today that I added my own portrait into a large letter "I". I see not why I should not be included: 'tis after all my travail and endurance which has created this art. I fear I went further still by adding a small joke. I depicted myself seated at my carrell, pen and parchment in hand. The parchment winds around the leaf stalk above and I inscribed the following words along its length:

Stella parens Solis, John Stell rege munere Prolis[37]

I realise this is rather impudent of me, but e'en now I wager 'tis a clever pun on my name. When 'tis read when my bones are rotting 'neath the soil people will remember me as a talented and clever scrivener.[38]

I trust, had I been able to make my own book, I could have been as great a scholar as Brother Jocelyn de Fournes. Although he died many years afore, he is still remembered in this abbey and at Rushen on the Isle of Man, as well as in the places where his work was commissioned by his patrons. He was a scholarly monk and translated and adapted ancient texts from the time before the great conquest[39]. He wrote of the lives of saints, translating from the ancient Anglo-Saxon tongue, recording their miracles and work for God.

35 St Benedict wrote The Rule which was a template for how the monks should behave.
36 To couch means to copy - Coucher Books are "copied" texts.
37 "O Star mother of the Sun, direct the favour of thy Son to John Stell". The two puns are stell/stella referring to John Stell and sun/son referring to Christ
38 Scrivener is another name for scribe
39 The Conquest was the Norman conquest in 1066, bringing a new regime of Norman barons

John Stell Scribe

His life of St Kentigern was writ for Jocelyn, Archbishop of Glasgow, St Waltheof for the abbey of Melrose, a gracious story of St Patrick for the Archbishop of Armagh and a historie of St Helena, for a nuns' community, for which we no longer have a name.

The light dims and I must clear away my work. Perchance nobody will notice my impertinent addition to the Coucher Book; if they do I will, no doubt have a weighty penance to perform. I will endeavour to work twice as hard tomorrow in an effort to hide what I have writ this day. Meantime, I must repair to the laver[40] to ready myself for the orders.

---

40 Washing area with sinks where the monks cleaned hands and faces before meals and services

CHAPTER 8

LAMBERT SIMNEL - 1523

Easy now, Molly, stay calm. There's no need to ruffle your feathers. M'Lady will want you looking your best when she takes you out later. As a hobby you may be small and not as powerful as the other hawks but you are her favourite, so let's smooth your feathers while you eat your mouse.

If it was up to me, of course, I'd have a peregrine: their speed when they stoop is truly spectacular; they are the prince of hawks ... Prince? Hmmm ...

Once upon a time I thought I may have my pick of hawks, as well as everything else. Thinking back to my boyhood and what was once promised me, I could have been the most powerful man in the land. King Edward would have been what I was known as. Just think of that, Molly, hardly believable now I am a mere falconer to a Lady. But those times remain clear in my mind, even though I was only ten summers old.

My life started as a baker's son in Suffolk, nothing special, and it continued that way until my tenth birthday when, for no good reason I could fathom at the time, a priest called Richard Symonds saw me and arranged with my parents that he be responsible for my education. For the next few months he taught me as if I were a courtier's son learning how to behave among gentlefolk – etiquette, some Latin phrases and even basic swordsmanship. I have to admit I rather enjoyed it and the pretensions it gave me.

Me pretentious? You would never have guessed, eh, Molly? Here, have this little titbit.

I was completely ignorant of Symonds' real reasons for choosing me at first: it was not until the end of 1486 that he explained to me that I was to pretend to be someone else. Gradually the truth was revealed to me. Symonds had thought I bore some semblance to the younger son of the late King Edward and wanted me to be the new boy king supported by the Yorkists[41]. He soon changed his mind, the Lord knows why, and decided I was to be the young Earl of Warwick who had a claim to the throne. He and some others took me across country and on a boat to Ireland where I was paraded around the streets on the shoulders of a huge man and an elaborate ceremony was arranged in which, crazy as it sounds, I was crowned in May 1487 in a huge cathedral there.

They said I was now King Edward VI! What do you think of that, Molly?

Lambert Simnel

To be honest, at that age, all this was like being in some sort of play, and I confess to enjoying being the centre of attention – what ten year old boy wouldn't? I had no awareness of the politics or the danger I was in – I just did as I was told and loved dressing up as a king.

Very soon after the coronation I was among many soldiers, mostly foreign ones, sailing back across the Irish Sea to England and we landed at a decent harbour on a tiny island called Pilla Fowdre[42], where a strong fortress looked out across the sea. The castle had been built, I discovered later, by the monks of nearby Furness Abbey, partly as defence against the Scots some time ago, partly as storage for their goods – I suspect some smuggling must have gone on[43] – and partly for their Abbott to get away from the work of the Abbey. It was a bleak place even though it was summer time but it had a beauty that has stayed with me all through the years since. I felt that, after all the crowds of Dublin, this was a break, almost a holiday like the ones the abbots had.

Mind you, the peace did not last as we were joined by hundreds, if not thousands of mercenary soldiers, some Irish, some German, some Flemish, who supported the Yorkists. There was no room on the island for us all, it is so small, but we did not stay more than a few nights as more troops arrived.

---

41 Following the Battle of Bosworth in 1485, when King Richard III was killed, it had been thought that the War of the Roses between the houses of Lancaster and York had finished, with Henry Tudor becoming King Henry VII, but followers of the House of York continued to plot against the new king.
42 Piel – there were several spellings in those days
43 By this time the monks were losing their piety and corruption was rife.

A small party of the soldiers explored the island for any sort of provisions before going back on small boats to their ships which were anchored in the deeper water, whereas Martin Schwartz, the leader of the troops, arranged for a few men-at-arms and myself to rest within the castle walls. The majority moved to the mainland on the second day and mustered at Swartsmoor[44] just a few miles north of the abbey. [45]

Back on the island we had a rough few nights with little sleep as the ground was rough, the seabirds loud and the weather rather inclement. However, I shall always remember that little island, not only for its beauty but as the last place I was able to rest before the disaster that followed. My short time there was definitely the lull before the storm.

But I'm getting ahead of myself, aren't I, Molly? Let me put you down here for a rest while I finish my tale. Where was I? Oh yes, on that little island in Lancashire[46].

Once we had rested we had to cross to the mainland. This meant sailing to another island, called Roa, just off the shore and, using low tide markers over a couple of days, walked across and up to join the new Irish troops and some local militia men led by one local nobleman, Sir Thomas Broughton, who were waiting at Swartsmoor. Here the main army gathered, maybe 8000 men, and we started our march south, full of hope and determination. We crossed the sands to Cartmeal and then to the east. Again I was the focus of attention on my horse with my small crown and the belief that I may actually become an accepted king of England grew as we travelled. I remember feeling excited among such a large army.

The excitement did fade somewhat on those long days of marching as we covered about forty miles a day, crossing the Pennines into our home base of Yorkshire where we had a small battle near the town of Tadcaster, beating a small group of Lancastrians. We continued south through Doncaster and into Sherwood Forest – more skirmishes slowed down our progress in both these places. While the small victories thrilled me, I remember seeing fighting up close and the horrors of the bloody wounds did frighten my ten year old self, I admit. But these were as nothing compared to what followed.

---

44 Swarthmoor
45 A note here to point out that the Abbey was put in a precarious position by the rebels landing on their island and the Abbot had to avoid any suggestion he had been supporting them. This is why he held aloof from them and kept away.
46 Of course, Furness was in Lancashire then.

We had not realised that King Henry, hearing about our rebellion, had been amassing a much larger army than ours and marching north to meet us. The two armies met to the east of Nottingham in fields near a place called East Stoke[47].

While I was protected at the rear of our soldiers I could still see some of what occurred and I was terrified at the vast number of arrows repeatedly fired by the Lancastrians towards us. Our mercenaries had little protection, wearing no armour, and were cut down in large numbers. It seemed to me that men were falling fast in front of me and any remnants of excitement were replaced by sheer terror as I feared for my life. I was certain I would die.

After just a couple of hours of this, our soldiers turned and fled but we were cornered in a narrow valley and even my personal men-at-arms bodyguard were killed. Luckily, one of the Lancastrian leaders realised that I was the "pretender" king and a mere boy and felt King Henry would like to meet the lad who wanted to replace him, so I was captured. They mocked me, laughing at my youth, as I was led past dreadful sights of bodies looking like hedgehogs[48] with so many arrows in them. I was shaking with fear and I confess to soiling myself at one point, which made the soldiers laugh all the more.

But I didn't die, did I, Molly?

The king showed me clemency as he realised I was a mere boy caught up in the rebellion. While so many of the Yorkist leaders were killed or – like my old teacher Richard Symonds – imprisoned, I was lucky; I was given a job by the king. I worked in the kitchens, at first turning the spit on which the meat was cooking, and later, as I grew, more demanding and skilled tasks. Yes, people laughed at me at first but that died down after a while and I worked hard until, one day, with some time on my hands, I came across the old King's falconer, Ned Turner. He saw that I was fascinated by the hawks and, as I came to visit him as often as time allowed, he asked if I would like to be his apprentice. Well, to be in the fresh air as opposed to the steaming hot kitchen, was a delight and Ned saw I took to my new skills well.

Yes, I moved in time from one noble house to another and in different parts of the country until I settled here[49] with my wife and son. And the rest, as they say, is history … real history!

Ah, here is M'Lady now. Come on, Molly, time for you to go hunting!

---

47 The Battle of Stoke Field was in truth the last battle of the War of the Roses
48 This analogy was made by the French poet, Jean Molinet, when he wrote about the battle.
49 Lambert never did reveal his final location

CHAPTER 9

WILLIAM CASE - 1531
Litigator Against Abbot Alexander Banke

I heard this morn that the wicked abbot Alexander Banke hath died. I cannot find the charity in my heart to mourn his passing and trust he will repent his ill doings at leisure in purgatory. He hath plagued this land for three score years and more, arriving here a young man of thirty summers. The parish priest at that time was excited and heralded his arrival with great stories of his standing and talents. The Father told us he was recommended by no other man than Abbot Marmaduke Huby of the great abbey of Fountains in Yorkshire, an honourable and saintly body. Banke was duly elected by the brethren and he was installed as abbot. Abbot Huby must have been most disappointed when he saw how his trust was so abused. The rogue Banke e'en put up the great west tower in his honour, a copy of "Huby's Tower" at Fountains; counterfeit like all that Banke did.

He arrived at our abbey, dressed well, with silk, fur trimmed cloak and the best harness and leather saddle money could buy. Dressed like a popinjay, which by his station outside the cloister he was permitted, but unseemly for a man of God. He brought with him rowdy varlets and young blades to roister with him and so began the misuse of his power. 'Twas as though the abbey was his manor in which he could rule and act as any lord. Aye and e'en the King himself could not have hunted more than he.

He found himself in grave peril when one of his schemes to gain land and fisheries brought him into conflict with the Earl of Derby. He had made such promises to his Lordship, which then he broke. His mistake in crossing the Earl was nearly his downfall, for he was a man of great power and wealth. He scarce escaped with his life, running like a hare to London with the abbey jewels. The Earl did attack our abbey with 2,000 men at arms, but to no avail for the bird was flown. Abbot Banke lost his seat but must have had some rare powerful friends because he was able to seize the abbacy, usurp the new abbot and throw the conspirators, so called, into gaol. This gave him great confidence and he then took up his course to steal more land and fill his coffers full of gold.

31

The love of the hunt and his desire for more land was the start of our troubles here in Sellergarth. 'Twas as humble a village as any other and we were not wealthy, but we were fed and housed most comfortably. The old abbot was a kind and generous Lord and never did he take more than his dues. He was e'en known to waive some tithes if our harvest was poor. With this in mind, we ne'er expected to find such a cruel master as this Banke fellow. He was ill content to hunt in the wide parkland, woods and fields which abound in our district. Oh nay! 'Twas not enough for him, he had to seize good pasture and arable land, and then he moved onto our small village.

His plan was to burn down the cottages and plough up the fields, drive off our animals and clear the cottagers. 'Twas no concern to him that we would have no homes to live in, no barns for our produce and no meadow for our sheep. He would have our land no matter what, to change into parkland for his jolly fellows to gallop across and chase down the deer and boar and for sheep cotes for the abbey. The village elders went to the abbey to plead our case, against the grain I must say, but we were begging for our homes… nay our lives! We arrived cap in hand at the gatehouse and most despairing. The porter admitted us after a goodly wait and we were led to the Almoner's lodge, where the poor are received. Old Harry Tyson who hath seen many an abbot was spitting bile. He thought this was a deliberate slight to us, reminding us that he, Alexander Banke held all the power and we-none! Perchance this was the notion, I cannot say, but it put us all in poor humour before my Lord Abbot did appear.

He swept in dressed in his abbot's weeds, all high quality, not the rough wool of his brothers' robes. He sat a' top of the wooden table and leaned back in his chair, elbows on the arms and his fingers pressed together in an arch, staring at us as if we were clods of clay from his boots. He smiled benignly. The smile remaining on his lips yet ne'er reaching his eyes. We set down our case before him and throughout, he smiled and nodded. All was civil until he began to laugh. A harsh and cruel laugh, rippling around the almonry. His prior bare stifled a smirk and the villagers looked perturbed.

Harry thumped his fist 'pon the table and demanded our claim be settled. The mood altered and 'twas all we could do to prevent violence breaking forth. I took the floor and spoke with calm and authority. Never before had I spoken thus. I warned the bloated cod's head to listen well. I warned him I would go to the court leet to gain a hearing, I knew this would displease him, he had many a litigation against him and the church did not look kindly on this. With one fierce glare he rose from his chair and stormed from the room.

William Case

I was as true as my word and did bring litigation against him. We thought we had outsmarted him and would save our village, but he was a wily old fox. Indeed, despite being the season of Advent, when we should have been preparing for the nativity of our Lord, he and his rufflers rode into the village on16th December. There were twenty-two ruffians, armed with cudgels and staves and turned the good people out, pulling down and burning our homes. These thieves and veritable rogues enclosed our mease[50] and other arable lands to give over to hunting and sheep cote for the abbey. We were bereft of hearth and home, made paupers for want of land and tenements. We gathered what goods and chattels we could and drove the livestock far down the valley in a sheltered dip below the hill which rises to Hietun[51]. Some of our number sought shelter in the homes of kin at Souerby[52] and Hietun. Those without kin built rough cotts with great haste, for the weather was fierce. We made the best we could but 'twas much less than we were accustomed to. The place in which we reside is known for its new barns, a small and simple settlement, yet Newbarns is no Sellergarth, being poorer. It was this which made me and Isabel my goodwife go forth and take our case to the Duchy Court[53].

This man Banke hath been afore the Duchy many times and we sought to gain recompense for our loss and impoverishment. This was many years past, back in 1516 and we did glean a meagre remuneration, but not enough to return us to our former prosperity. Yet Banke, he went forth as though nought was amiss. He had no honour nor conscience and he continued in his dissolute ways as before. I hear his burial is to be a grand affair, befitting his great station. These monks are superstitious and will not risk nay saying his funerary desires. His character demands he be thrown in unconsecrated ground, yet tis likely he will rest in the holiest place in the abbey church, no doubt dressed in silk and sable, bejewelled and posed as a great man of faith. His deeds cannot be expunged. They will be remembered and with God's good grace his remains forgot and unknown to those who follow.

---

50 Mease refers to farmland
51 Hawcoat a village mentioned in the Domesday Book
52 Sowerby a wood and small settlement
53 Duchy Court of Lancaster

CHAPTER 10

ROGERUS PYLE[54] THE LAST ABBOT
Dissolution 9th April 1537

"I Rogerus by the providence of God, Abbot of the monastery of St Mary of Furness in the county of Lancaster" the words stick in my throat… "surrender up unto the hands of the lord the King, that now is, Henry Vlll, by the Grace of God, King of England and France, Defender of the Faith, Lord of Ireland and head upon earth of the Anglican church, our monastery…"[55] This concoction is drawn up by Thomas Cromwell's[56] creatures for the enrichment of the King's power. We have no choice, lest we sacrifice our lives by opposing this abomination. 'Tis a brave man who would gainsay the King, e'en those close to him and greater and more educated than I, quake to disagree on this point. Those who do meet a bloody end. Sir Thomas More,[57] who was close to the King and a friend and mentor was not spared when he refused to sign the Oath of Supremacy making Henry the Supreme Head of the Anglican church. His head rolled from the block just as any other common traitor's would, his poor remains displayed 'pon London Bridge on a pike; the only mercy that he was spared the traitor's execution of hanging, drawing and quartering.

I have seen those who object suffer so, the poor Carthusian monks of Charterhouse who were cruelly put to death at Tyburn and spared no mercy as More had been. Even closer the Abbot of Whalley, John Paslew, only this year executed in Lancaster for his disobedience and following the fool Robert Aske in his doomed Pilgrimage of Grace[58]. This enterprise claimed many more, close to home: the sub-prior and several canons of Cartmel Priory as well as unfortunate souls who supported them, were all of them, hanged. Therefore, I

---

54 Rogerus Pyle or Pele, last abbot of Furness
55 Extract from the Deed of Surrender
56 Henry Vlll's Chief Minister
57 Henry Vlll's Lord High Chancellor, later made a Saint by the Pope for his martyrdom
58 Robert Aske led a protest about the Act of Supremacy; he was hanged in chains at York in 1537

have counselled my monks to stay their tongues and quietly accept the decree of dissolution. I favour following the Prior of Cartmel, who absconded to the Crown forces under Earl Derby than his canons who now lay mouldering in unmarked graves. Some call me coward, but I prefer expedient.

'Tis not as though I did not try to save our monastery. Nay I did all in my power and it cost me a pretty penny too in bribes. When I arrived at Furness to take up the abbacy after the death of that dissolute rogue, Alexander Banke,[59] I was filled with enthusiasm and good cheer. Sadly, the monks I found here were either apathetic and lazy or rabble rousers. I had been gratified that Master Cromwell had chosen me to hold this great abbey, but it soon became clear to me that I was a dupe who he believed to be weak and malleable. I was foolish enough to pay him £200 to secure my admission and a small annual pension; I curse myself, but he is one who should not be crossed. I am sure he has had his poor opinion of me confirmed ever since. I attempted to coax him into understanding that the abbey was not corrupt and venal, and that we perform good service to the poor people and provide goodly service to God. Each time I wrote, I flattered him and sent gifts of money and gold, from the abbey coffers, but from my own purse too. I do not know why I thought he would look kindly on me or on this abbey, for I know him well from my time at the Chancery[60]. He has always been unbending, pitiless and overly ambitious. I have long suspected he has secret Protestant leanings and, now he has the ear of the King, he might well achieve his dream of reforming the church. He walks a dangerous path, for Henry is no reformer. He still names himself Defender of the Faith and maintains his catholic beliefs. His only grievance is with his Holiness the Pope and the wealth of the church in England. Henry craves the wealth and land of the abbeys and sees it as taking back what is his - as many of the lands gifted to the church came from his royal forebears. Of course, the witch Nan Bullen[61] has likely charmed him with her spells, for she too is of the reforming religion and long desired the death of the true queen, Katherine[62] and hungered for the crown for herself.

Our brethren are dismayed, three of our number arrested and sent to the gaol at Lancaster Castle, as they were found to have supplied money for the rebels of the Pilgrimage. We sincerely pray they will escape with their lives. The others, though dissenting, will not speak out and all joined together this day with the prior and myself to sign the Deed of Surrender before the King's officers and

---

59 The penultimate abbot of Furness, a rogue and a troublemaker
60 The Lord Chancellor's Office in London
61 Better known as Anne Boleyn Henry's second wife
62 Katherine of Aragon Henry's first wife

Rogerus Pyle

the Earl of Sussex. We gathered solemnly in our beautiful Chapter House and met together as our community for the final time. Each one of the twenty-eight monks signed their names and the Prior and I added ours. 'Tis a painful day for us and one which will be spoken of for many a year.

One Robert Southwell, an officer of the Crown with his creature Thomas Holcroft, are to come in June to oversee the destruction of the abbey and to liquidate the assets to bolster the King's coffers. Southwell regards us with contempt and he looks at us with disapproval. I fear he will make Furness an example and nought will be left; we are the very first of the large houses to be dissolved. Many of the smaller houses have already gone and their communities dispersed. With no provision for the poor, the aged and the infirm there is death and disease ahead. The monks and nuns will not all be able to find employment, the frail amongst them will become destitute and add to the poor. I pray that the Commissioner will care for the abbey servants as he has promised, their wages are in arrears and their homes like the monks are abbey buildings. I will repair to the parish of Dalton and become the vicar. The previous incumbent fled at the time of the Pilgrimage of Grace and his living is now vacant. Master Cromwell has in graciousness allowed me the position as vicar, and I will have a meagre stipend, but I realise I am fortunate. I will as a matter of courtesy and pragmatism still send small gifts of money to assure his continued good favour.

As I wander through the cloister, I contemplate what it will be like when the despoilers come and begin to remove the goods and chattels. Once the abbey is stripped and the monks sent off the fabric will be torn asunder and sold or reused, the parkland and fields sold, the mills and granges reassigned to those in the favour of the King and all trace of our opus dei[63] erased and in time forgot! I shall be glad to be in my new ministry so that I do not see the wanton and sacrilegious destruction. I fear God's wrath will be served upon the King for this dark act. God protect and save his Majesty and give him guidance and forgiveness.

---

63 Opus dei - Latin for "God's work" the work of the monastery

CHAPTER 11

THOMAS HOLCROFT 1538

Right, today we start. I have been looking forward to this for many a day. It's about time those damned lazy monks of Furness were kicked out and their precious building destroyed. Like their fellows in other abbeys around the country they have disgraced their calling with their smuggling, corruption and forceful treatment of the people. Why, one has only to look at the present abbot's predecessor, the villain Banke, to see that nowadays the most irreligious men become monks and even abbots. They claim they obey a vow of poverty but many are rich beyond the imagination of ordinary folk. They act more as developers of the site than brothers of God and have far too much power.

But now good King Henry, as Defender of the Faith, is changing all that. I, Thomas Holcroft, am the local agent of my Lord the King who is in great need of the huge wealth these corrupt so-called men of the cloth have acquired over recent years. He asked Thomas Cromwell to appoint commissioners to visit all monasteries and examine their work and wealth and one commissioner reported that "the Furness monks had been of as evil hearts and minds as any other." I myself visited the Abbey some months ago and saw this was true. So now I am under orders to make the abbey uninhabitable and I am going to totally destroy that symbol of their time and take the valuables for the King's coffers. A joyous task indeed.

The present abbot, Rogerus Pele, has been clever and officially surrendered to save his skin, unlike the canons of Cartmel just across the sands who we recently hanged, but he is not able to save the building and its riches. He handed over the abbey's extensive riches to be the property of the Crown, which made things easier for us, before he was moved to be vicar of nearby Daltoun.

Some of the monks were cunning and accepted payments of up to £80 to leave the abbey quietly rather than resist and others were given, generously in my opinion, the sum of two pounds to buy new clothes to replace their habits. Some,

I hear, gained posts as clerical workers in the local parishes or as tutors for the sons of the gentry; others became farm workers. The old and sick monks in the infirmary were also given money as they were turned out. Lay monks became farm workers again and the boys from the cloister school were simply told to go home and not to return. The only people I felt sorry for were the workmen employed by the abbey and the poor who had been fed by the monks … but there were bound to be some that suffered from the change and we did provide work for a few weeks for many of the workers.

So, here we are – I say "we" because I have my own men plus many labourers from the area employed to help with the demolition – it's an indication of what local people of Furness think of the monks that they are willing to be employed to destroy their abbey!

Luckily it is the month of July so summer weather helped us in our work. The first job is to strip the lead from the roofs; for this is extremely valuable. This means erecting our engines [64] to enable the men to reach it. For this we cut down some of the many trees hereabouts and fashioned them into strong poles and platforms. I had an excellent engineer with me who supervised the building of the structure which had to be strong yet able to be moved around the building. Then he added a pulley at the top with ropes, hook and a bucket to lower the lead in pieces to the ground. This was an essential but time-consuming process but did bring much of value for our collection.

Below, meanwhile, the windows were smashed and the lead taken from them and the lower buildings broken up bit by bit. Once the lead was removed from the roofs, it was taken into the old nave of the church where a large fire was made to melt it into "pigs" or ingots. Once in suitable sizes it was loaded into carts and taken away to be used for the King's purposes.

Over the next few weeks, we destroyed the rest of the structure bit by bit, leaving piles of the red stone lying around for any local farmer to take away and use for barns or whatever. The bell tower, being so high, took more pains to destroy but, with the use of ropes and other engines, we managed to bring it down. We did not destroy any outer buildings away from the main church because we were happy again for farmers to use them.

In total, almost £800 was grossed from the abbey's suppression but only £367 remained after all the various costs were paid. As well as the monks' handouts, these included paying off the monastery's debts, which came to £98, the stripping

---

64 Includes basic wooden scaffolding and ropes and pulleys

and casting of the lead [£70] and, of course, our expenses of £102. We sold the bells to some men of Kendal for the fine sum of £80 too.

Once we had ensured the building was not habitable or suitable for use by monks once more, and everything valuable was removed, I was happy to leave local people to complete the destruction and take away what they wanted. I imagine many farms and other buildings in the area would make use of the abbey's stonework for decades to come. I am delighted to have helped ordinary folk in this way.

The final task I also left to others, that was the sale of the farm animals, equipment and provisions in the abbey granges round and about. Cromwell passed on that the King was not interested in the trivial amounts of money these would bring so I left instructions that the proceeds of the sales were to be brought to me at my lodgings where I am sure I would find a use for them!

And so, at the beginning of August in the year of our Lord 1537 our work was done. Before I left for London I took one last look at the ruins of Furness Abbey and I smiled at a job well done.

Thomas Holcroft

41

CHAPTER 12

SIR JOHN PRESTON
First Baronet Preston 1645

Through their own efforts and with the patronage of members of the nobility, our family have been fortunate in the last two generations in acquiring much land and other assets. There were the farms near Sourby Wood[65], a fishing area on the isle of Walney and pasture land at Ireleth Cot among others. Over the years these acquisitions brought us increasing wealth and our lives became more comfortable. I remain grateful to my ancestors and aware of the responsibility this places on my shoulders to continue the stewardship of our lands.

My grandfather, who shared the same name as myself, at first leased the land around the ruins of Furness Abbey from the Crown, inheriting the lease from his father-in-law, Sir Thomas Curwen, and later he owned it all outright. It was he and his brother, Sir Thomas Preston, who built the Manor House on the northern side of the ruins for our family home, a place I grew up in and loved very much.

Firstly, its location is so tranquil in the Vale of Beckansgill with the smell of garlic in the spring and so many flowers among the trees. And of course, the ruins of the abbey were my playground as a child as for my children now. Such a sense of history and peace it has that Jane and I love living here. We can walk on the path into Dalton to church or to visit friends, and the servants can collect produce from the market there.

Secondly, the house itself is magnificent and wonderful for entertaining which I am delighted to do as part of my duties since being ennobled[66] last year. I have added many new features, including paintings and furniture and am wondering about extending the house in the next year or so to accommodate more guests[67].

---

65 Sowerby Wood
66 Sir John was made a Baronet in 1644
67 Sir John died later in 1645 before any extension was built

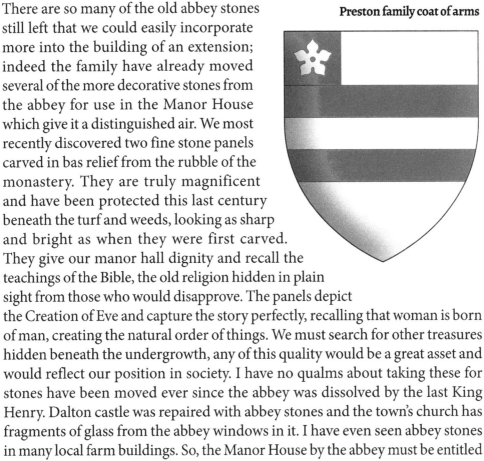

There are so many of the old abbey stones still left that we could easily incorporate more into the building of an extension; indeed the family have already moved several of the more decorative stones from the abbey for use in the Manor House which give it a distinguished air. We most recently discovered two fine stone panels carved in bas relief from the rubble of the monastery. They are truly magnificent and have been protected this last century beneath the turf and weeds, looking as sharp and bright as when they were first carved. They give our manor hall dignity and recall the teachings of the Bible, the old religion hidden in plain sight from those who would disapprove. The panels depict the Creation of Eve and capture the story perfectly, recalling that woman is born of man, creating the natural order of things. We must search for other treasures hidden beneath the undergrowth, any of this quality would be a great asset and would reflect our position in society. I have no qualms about taking these for stones have been moved ever since the abbey was dissolved by the last King Henry. Dalton castle was repaired with abbey stones and the town's church has fragments of glass from the abbey windows in it. I have even seen abbey stones in many local farm buildings. So, the Manor House by the abbey must be entitled to some also.

All in all, the family love living here and we [Jane especially] have made the Manor House into a splendid home; in fact I was rather upset when a guest last week, meaning to compliment me, said that he could see the Manor House as a first class inn one day. As it is now the ancestral home of the Prestons I do hope that day never comes.[68]

---

68 The Manor House did indeed become the Furness Abbey Hotel two hundred years later; see later chapters.

CHAPTER 13

THE WHITE LADY 1665

A GHOSTLY TALE

The Lady

I have awaited the return of my dearest love for so long, I almost lose track of the days. All I can do is wander the grounds of Furness Abbey, retracing the paths we walked hand in hand. Now and again, I pause to look around, in case he has returned. Then I fall to tears, many bitter tears and I fade away…

∗∗∗∗

The Shepherd

I tend my flock among the ruins in summer, for 'tis pleasant wandering among the moss-covered stones. A peace settles upon me and I thank God that the Great Rebellion[69] has passed at last. 'Twas a time of horror, brother against brother, father against son, the right order of the world upturned, and churches defiled. Sir John[70] was much acclaimed for his support of the King, God rest his soul and he raised much silver for the cause. Sir John Maney, and his troops came for the manorial rents from Furness Abbey and were driven from the land by the men of Furness who fraternised with the Parliamentary fleet, anchored off the Pile of Fouldray. There was a skirmish but one mile from Sir John Preston's manor, in a field at Dalton, many soldiers being trapped and killed in the pinfold nearby.

---

69 English Civil War
70 Sir John Preston

The fighting was harsh and poor Sir John[71] was brought down from his horse, which was killed. He being down was knocked on the head; his perfect sense and understanding ne'er recovered for some half year after.

Not long after the end of the Great Rebellion, Sir John Preston, as many others of the King's men did, made peace with the new Parliament. 'Twas an uneasy peace as Sir John would not renounce his faith and he was declared "delinquent".

During this troubled time, he was heard to lament the deaths of his most faithful servants in the struggle. He long despaired when he saw the young lady, bereft of her betrothed gentleman, killed in service to Sir John, wandering the abbey in grief. She is just one young person lost and damaged by war most uncivil.

****

The hours hang heavy, day blends into night, each one the same as the last. I have wandered here each day; he hath promised to return and I must be here awaiting. I pray he comes today. I prayed he came yesterday. But he is not here. He left resplendent in his wide brimmed hat, trimmed with a feather as bright as a peacock, his wavy brown hair touching the fine lace collar and his beard shaped like the King into a point. His sword slung from his leather belt which matched the high boots he wore o'er his breeches showed his purpose and determination to serve his king. I well recall his gallant smile as he rode away... but where is he now? He must return.

My hopes fade. He is not coming. I still pray for his safest return. I walk in his footsteps across the church and past the stream. I sense his presence but see him not. As I wander in the moonlight beneath the willows and along the path to the wood, I hear the night cry of the owl. An evil portent for sure; it cannot mean I will ne'er see him again. I stand in our special place, o'erlooking the pale shapes of the abbey, sacred and silent, where once we plighted our troth handfasted each other for all eternity. I bear his ring still and wear the white silken gown which most becomes me for his delight. 'Tis worn and tattered now and I waste away beneath it, growing thinner each day. But if I should repair to home, I might miss his return. My hair is flecked with silver, like the moon and my flesh is white like the bones barely concealed beneath. I know not how long I have roamed this stately sepulchre; my voice is stolen by sadness and my cries are hushed. I search for him to no avail...

---

71 Preston

The White Lady

The Shepherd's Wife

I took such a fright this eve. The moon was full, bathing all in silver light, the gloomy trees bending in holy reverence and the night creatures stirring. From our li'le cot we see the shady profile of the abbey and its presence governs the valley yet. A silence descends and peace reigns over us all. Yet tonight, there did seem an unsettling miasma about the place, a scent of days gone by and shimmering contours which were out of nature and all that is wholesome. Indeed, I had bethought to place a talisman above the door to ward off the evil spirits which abound at night.

I chanced to see something within the shadows of the ruins. I supposed at first that it was my husband wending home from the high pastures, a glimpse of light flitting like a firefly, which I took to be his lantern. The bairns were abed in the loft, tucked up safely and fast asleep, so I reached for my shawl and wrapped it round me to venture outside. I know the path so well I did not wait to light a lantern - I can feel my way like a cat in the dark. The firelight and candle glow would light me home, and I would have Tom beside me. I strolled across to the old chapel, for I wager that is what it was, having popish carving and an altar step for the old mass. The bats were out, noiselessly gliding about the trees and catching insects. All was silence and the air was still. I saw a swift movement beyond the beck and beneath the willows; my heart skipped: it must be dear Tom, I supposed.

The clouds darkened the moon's silver disc momentarily and darkness bathed the path in inky blackness. I stopped for a moment and waited for the moon's gentle light to shine and light my way again. My feet were rooted to the very ground, anchored as soundly as any of the trees beside me. The tiny hairs upon my neck and arms stood up and my blood ran cold in my veins. There at the top of the path to the wood stood a figure, one which I had not seen before and one which I pray I will ne'er see more.

She stood, draped in white tatters, a bridal dress no doubt, yet ruined and ragged, wrapped wraith-like around her spare body. She made no sound but wrung her hands and the cries she made stifled in her poor throat. She looked around her seeking someone long lost and sore missed. I tried to speak and ask her what she sought, but she turned towards me, unseeing. She drifted it seemed, and floated along the path, beneath the willows and past me towards the abbey. I was afeared that some witchcraft might be afoot, yet I felt her sadness and that she posed no threat to me. I followed at a distance and she reached the old tower where the monks of old rang their bells for holy mass. There she reached out in despair and fell to the ground. As I drew closer, her whiteness shimmered and faded into nothing. I stared at the place and cold chills ran down my spine like cold newly drawn water.

My heart beat hard, and my mouth was dry. I could not countenance this ghostly appearance any longer. I turned and ran, stumbling over bricks and masonry until I reached our cottage. I closed the door and I confess I crossed myself like a papist, to ward off any evil which might have followed me. I rested uneasily and my mind returned to the images I had seen, over and over again. 'Twill be a long time afore I venture out at dusk or dark again. I cannot wait for Tom to return, though he will chastise me for a silly goose for such wild imaginings.

CHAPTER 14

FATHER THOMAS WEST
Author of *Antiquities of Furness* 1774

It is with great satisfaction that I lay down my pen this day. It has been a work of great effort and a desire to bring to life the abbey of the Blessed Saint Mary in Furness. A tear comes to my eye when I think of those magnificent conventual ruins and wonder how the brothers felt when the heretic King Henry dissolved their monastery. As a Jesuit priest I cannot but mourn this great loss, indeed, a loss replicated throughout this land and heralding in a new religion and abandoning our true faith. I studied much in my travels in Europe and was availed of great learning and philosophies. It is only now, in my later years that I find the time to pursue my own discovery of natural philosophy and the history of this place.

Antiquities of Furness

I am most fortunate that the benefactor, Sir Thomas Preston, gave Tytup Hall[72] to the sole use of our Jesuit order. He was a devout Catholic and recusant[73], which his noble forebears were too, despite having gained the monastery and its lands at the great suppression. They might have hid' their true beliefs, in Tudor times for it was a time of turmoil and great persecution. He became a Jesuit himself but left behind this sanctuary for our use.

---

72 Tytup Hall a mansion just outside Dalton
73 Recusant - one who refused to submit to the authority of the church

Naturally, I have availed myself of the other property in the gift of his family, to whom much of the old abbey lands belong. The dedication in my *Antiquities of Furness* is to my Lord George Cavendish[74] who has assisted in this Topographical Account of Furness not to flatter but to return the gratitude necessary for his choice and arrangements of materials availed unto me. And, as I remark in my Dedication, his noble family remain "affected to the preservation" and "guard the precious ruins from decay."

I have spent many hours in the Vale of Nightshade wandering amidst the ruins of Furness Abbey. 'Tis a fair walk from here, through hill and dale, passing through the market town of Dalton and thence along the old monks' way through the Haggs and past the mill. About one mile to the south of Dalton stands the Abbey of Furness, magnificent in its ruins.

The once grand manor house, built from stone taken from the ruins, lays neglected and is a lowly farmhouse these days. It sits aside the lane and at the head of the vale.

An ancient arch straddles the road close by to an old chapel, beyond which is the spectacle of the abbey itself. I never fail to be impressed by this vista, despite the growth of shrubs and trees among the red sandstone. It is still possible to view the shape of the buildings and define in which part of the holy edifice we stand. Grass and moss invade the sacred spaces and piles of stones litter the grounds. It is easy to see where the local people removed the stones for their own humble homes and barns. The fine carvings and effigies lie cast down and neglected, echoes of the beauty which must have adorned church and cloister.

The tombs of mailed Knights and Barons are broken and disturbed; the spirits of those unfortunate souls must wander from their resting place seeking the peace they thought they had assured for all eternity.

---

74 Cavendish inherited the abbey through a union via the Preston /Lowther branch

There too are some humbler grave covers, cracked with ancient names carved and long forgot, Latin script grooved upon the limestone. All is ruin and decorous decay half hid' from the modern world.

I had discourse yesterday with the old shepherd who has made it his habit to rest behind the great east window. His sheep graze throughout the grounds and keep down the undergrowth. I have made careful drawings of the plan of the buildings and some etchings will appear in the book. A thorough survey should be made, but this is for others to undertake.

'Tis rare to find remnants of the monks themselves, as their riches are long ago removed. Those fragments of fine glass and carvings that remain are concealed 'neath the clay and grass. Some evidence of the carving is still to be seen; the magnificent sedilia, that bench for the high officiants of the mass, is sublime. The rich carving is perfect and preserved, the canopied stalls witness the skill of those ancient masons; yet despoilers have left their mark too, names graven into the sandstone to rest there for all eternity, unchallenged and as forgotten as the monks.

The range of Norman arches are resplendent and still sharp in their ornamentation. There is a pleasing outlook and surely one of the best panoramas of a medieval monastery e'er seen. I must rest awhile now. I am quite fatigued. I pray that his Lordship finds satisfaction in this volume and that it is well received in scholarly circles.

The East PROSPECT of the Ruins of Furness Abbey in LANCASHIRE.

THOMAS ALCOCK BECK
Author of *Annales Furnesienses* 1844

My health has all but overcome me, confined as I am in my invalid chair. My spine which prevented me from being a young man from walking did not prevent the agility of my mind. I have taken many years to complete my work and finally *Annales Furnesienses* is to be published. There will be a limited issue of some 250 copies, which, with each copy priced at only seven guineas, might prove to make a financial loss. Of course, it was not for profit that I embarked on this endeavour, I am a passionate antiquarian and am keen to carry on the work of such scholars as Father West and the talented young doctor William Close.

West made prodigious efforts to capture the history of the Abbey of St Mary of Furness and the wider landscapes. He has been heralded as the first to do this and Close took it upon himself to add to the work and produced a new edition in 1805, adding to it many articles on the botany of the area, archaeology, and geology. In truth he enriched the history and included eighty-six additional pages. He involved himself in physical surveys of the ruins and uncovered many explanations and interpretations of the incomprehensible jumble of ruins.

The poor fellow had not the time to complete the *Itinerary of Furness and Environs* which would most likely have rivalled West's *Guide to the Lakes*. I took it upon myself to edit this illustrious work for posterity. Close was a polymath, a Renaissance man of his time, being well disposed to science, medicine, and philosophy. He invented hydraulic pumping systems and many solutions for the betterment of society. Indeed, he saved many lives at the village of Rampside by instigating the vaccination for smallpox in 1722, eliminating the disease with the new science invented by Edward Jenner. He could not save himself, however, and succumbed to consumption in 1813 aged only thirty-six. I still have much to do before time runs out for me too and have collected much material and documents for a history of North Lonsdale, Cartmel and the Priory of Conishead. It is to be hoped I am granted that time and can complete these studies.

My "Annales Furnesienses" is dedicated to Her Majesty Queen Victoria and provides a most comprehensive edition of the history of St Mary of Furness. I have spared no expense and each volume has fine engravings and careful transcripts of the important documents of the monastery. The look of the finished book is quite sumptuous and finely crafted, and I am pleased with it. I am indebted to the Earl of Burlington for his permission to excavate at the abbey, providing us invaluable insight into the conventual buildings and church.

To the untrained eye the grassy mounds and depressions mean nought, but on close inspection they reveal the rich past of the order of Cistertians[75] and even before. The moss encrusted ruins lie broken against the quarry, and the streams still meander across the vale untouched by time. Yet these ruins demonstrate to us how frail our human enterprises become and how these institutions fade and die.

I have filled my time with these studies and allayed the tedium of my invalidity. I have directed exploration of the abbey and its holdings, discovering the hidden treasures, and cataloguing these. We have discovered much, and this will inform us of the true nature and living of the Cistertians. The charters and documents which I have been privy too have revealed much of the business and events of those holy men.

I trust my efforts will not be wasted and pray that the abbey remains protected for many years hence. For now, my work is done, but I will resume my other projects as soon as I am able.

---

75 Earlier spelling of Cistercians

CHAPTER 15

BIG BOB STEETON
Railway Navvy 1844

Of course, it were 'ard work. Wha' else could it be, working twelve hours a day wi' me Lord Lovel[76] often moving twenty tons o' muck? But ah'd known nowt else. Me da' had been a navvy and me granda before him worked on t' canals – it were wha' we did.

Ah came fro' a village near Keighley in Yorkshire, but ever since ah were a lad, ah'd been on the tramp[77] followin' t'work. Ah always did the heavy work 'cos ah'm a big lad and used to pickin' up rocks – t'were a lot of that in buildin' railways. Nearly twenty years ah've been doin' this, since ah were fifteen, and ah've been back ha'am only twice in all those years.

For this latest job ah've come across to Lancashire to work on the new railway line that goes from the town of Dalton to the port at Barrow-in-Furness. The setup is like most ah've worked at – we sleep in wooden huts, ten of us here [ah once had to share with fifteen other blokes] but this time we lodged wi' t'Baxendales, a family of four who rented the hut on Barrow Island from the contractor. John Baxendale was t' Billy Gorman[78] so we had to make sure we were on time – we don't want any more deducted from our pay. One word from John was enough for any of us t'lose some sugar 'n' honey[79] so ah was keen to get to work early. Ah could have paid my penny ha'penny[80] for a night in a bed but ah don't mind t'floor which is cheaper – ah pay just a penny for five nights.

---

76 Shovel. Navvies had their own rhyming slang.
77 *On the tramp* was the term for going where the work was, tramping around the country.
78 Foreman
79 Money
80 In the old money – 1.5d – equivalent of 1p today.

Bob Steeton

Some folk think we navvies get paid well but remember, we never get t' full pay. Three shillin's a day we are supposed to get. But, as well as rent, we have to buy our food from t'company meal caravans, where t'Pig's ear[81] is watered and pies disgusting. And we need big meals for t'work we 'ave t'do. We eat bacon, potatoes, bread and t'beer for breakfast, dinner and tea, an' lots of it. All this 'as to be paid for so there's not much brass left at end of t'week.

T'work itself was hard of course but better than some other sites . No tunnels, thank God, on this stretch – tunnellin' killed many of me mates – for the one needed had already been done and t'tradesmen in workshops got t'wooden sleepers and the rail out on time. But first we had t'blast cuttings, for example alongside t'wood by Furness Abbey. The blasting itself was for other, more skilled, men but we then had to remove tons of stone and level t'ground for the rails. If weather were good, this was not too bad but in heavy rain the red soil quickly became reet thick mud and us fellas could not work so fast. We worked while there was light enough, so more hours in summer, not so many in winter.

While working by t'abbey, I would often ta'e me bait[82] and beer, and eat sitting on t'stones in there. It were reet peaceful under t'old walls and somehow we would stay quiet more in there than anywhere else … for a while, anyroads. Last week when 'ere ah felt ah wanted to leave my mark, as t'were. Not really sure why, ah simply felt the need. So ah waited till other blokes had gone and picked up a sharp piece of flint and marked my initials on one of the walls. Ah wonder how long that'll last.

We 'ad some bad news today. "Policeman" Jack is dead. It's 'ard to believe as he was such a big character in our group. Very rough and ready and as 'ard as nails, 'e was t'only bloke who could match me both in fightin' and in shovellin'. We named him "policeman" after the puppet in Punch and Judy for 'e was just as likely to use a stick as 'is fists when brawlin'. The two of us would often go off on a randy[83] together, and we nearly always ended up in a fight whether with other navvies or with some of t'local lads who hate us. Ah'd not seen 'im for a few days and had not heard 'e was ill; it seems he caught the dreaded cholera which can knock even the biggest fellas down. Poor Jack. At least, like me, 'e was a single bloke and had no family left behind.

We do lose a lot of fellas in this job; some like Jack get illnesses, some from accidents. It's much worse when tunnelin' of course, where gas, falls down

---

81 Beer
82 Packed lunch
83 "Going on a randy" meant going for a drinking spree.

airshafts and collapses can be added to t'truck's hitting blokes on the tramway, landslips and illnesses that can hit us all. Ah've known dozens of fellas who have died as navvies. Who knows, it may well get me one day, but it's the only life ah know so ah have to carry on. Mebbe, that's why we drink so much, knowin' we may not last long; ah have five or more pints of beer a day, more at the weekend, but that and smoking me clay pipe are the only pleasures ah get.

Reet, it's time to get back at it. Hobnail overshoes on, a few pennies in one pocket and pipe and baccy in t'other, off to cart another few tons of stone away. Ah 'eard a visitor call us "unsung heroes" last week … ah sure don't feel like a bloody hero!

CHAPTER 16

WILLIAM WORDSWORTH 1846

The Editor

Westmorland Gazette

Kendal

April 11 1846

Sir,

It is known and accepted that I have long had a fondness - nay, I may call it love - for the High Church of St Mary, known as Furness Abbey. Ever since the time during my schooling days in Hawkshead nearly fifty years past, when I first borrowed a horse and rode to the Vale of Beckansgill, also called the Vale of Deadly Nightshade because of the flowers that bloom there, it has held a power over my imagination. Indeed, I have visited it many times since, and have written in tribute:

> *Of Nightshade, to St. Mary's honour built,*
>
> *Stands yet a mouldering pile with fractured arch.*

I particularly recall that, whilst staying with cousin Elizabeth at Rampside, in, I think, the year 1797, I toured the area of Furness more thoroughly. I especially admired from there the view of Piel Island ... I later wrote:

> *I was thy neighbour once, thou rugged Pile!*
>
> *Four summer weeks I dwelt in the sight of thee:*
>
> *I saw thee every day; and all the while,*
>
> *Thy form was sleeping on a glassy sea.*

I also stayed with our friends, the Baldwins at Aldingham Rectory, from where I crossed the sands to see the Priory at Cartmel. However, it is the ruins of Furness Abbey which have stayed with me the most. I wish most fervently that I had the strength to go there once more.

Perhaps you may permit an old man, even one as successful and well known as I, and made Laureate by Her Majesty herself, to reproduce in your pages some verses I wrote about the place:[84]

> *Here, where, of havoc tired and rash undoing,*
>
> *Man left this Structure to become Time's prey,*
>
> *A soothing spirit follows in the way*
>
> *That Nature takes, her counter-work pursuing.*
>
> *See how her Ivy clasps the sacred Ruin,*
>
> *Fall to prevent or beautify decay;*
>
> *And, on the mouldered walls, how bright, how gay,*
>
> *The flowers in pearly dews their bloom renewing!*
>
> *Thanks to the place, blessings upon the hour;*
>
> *Even as I speak the rising Sun's first smile*
>
> *Gleams on the grass-crowned top of yon tall Tower*
>
> *Whose cawing occupants with joy proclaim*
>
> *Prescriptive title to the shattered pile,*
>
> *Where, Cavendish, thine seems nothing but a name!*

I hope you may accept from these lines that my affection for the Abbey is genuine and sincere, nor am I the only one. The Picturesque[85] movement, from the time of Gilpin[86] in the last century, has attracted many artists and writers to visit the

---

84 Included in his partly biographical poem, "The Prelude" 1805
85 The Picturesque movement was a style of looking at a scene in a romantic manner, seeing what is beautiful and sublime in it and often exaggerating these elements.
86 William Gilpin was a Cumberland artist who, in 1772, toured the county and first coined the phrase "picturesque". He particularly liked ruins and Furness Abbey was a favourite of his.

Abbey and appreciate its beauty. JMW Turner[87] came and made several sketches of the ruins, among others. I have even heard that Her Majesty Queen Victoria is planning a visit soon.[88]

Bearing all this in mind, and understanding that my passion has always been to see the relationship between man and nature as central to my view of the world, I come to the main purpose of my letter. Furness Abbey is a man-made structure, even one also despoiled by man, in a very natural setting. When one looks down upon it in its vale with trees and flowers around, one cannot be comprehend that the two fit so perfectly well together, man's creation in its natural background.

However, now that perfect balance has been destroyed, for a new man-made creation has entered the tranquil scene and one that certainly does nothing to enhance the picturesque feeling of the Abbey. I refer, of course, to the damned railway, which is in the process of destroying all that is beautiful there. Moreover, since a station at the Abbey has opened about eighteen months ago, the number of tourists is likely to increase, ruining the tranquillity of the place.

Public domain image

William Wordsworth
1839 watercolor by Margaret Gillies

In addition, not only does any train passing through present a visual blot on the scene when viewed, with billowing smoke pouring out from the ugly locomotive, but its noise assaults the ears too. If one is sitting in quiet contemplation, maybe in a "pensive mood" among the stones, imagining the monks centuries ago, then to be suddenly disturbed by one of these railway engines blasting by will surely demolish one's creative thoughts as much as King Henry demolished the stones. Furthermore, I fear for the future of the Abbey itself as these engines that blight our senses could also be literally undermining the ruins themselves. The frequent vibrations over a period of time could well disturb the foundations of the walls for the iron rails are within yards of the Chapter House itself. Soft stone on soft ground with regular vibrations: how long before the walls suffer and perhaps collapse?

---

87 JMW Turner, the great painter, did sketch the abbey in 1797 but did not turn any into full paintings.
88 Queen Victoria did indeed visit in 1848.

I do not blame the men who build the railway – they are poor things whose lower intellect cannot be expected to appreciate either the joy of solitude nor the effects of what they have done. I blame the decision of those above them – they are the real "profane despoilers!"

Sir, I hope you will be willing to publish this epistle in your esteemed journal as you have published many of mine previously, whether on this or on other topics.

I remain your servant,

W. WORDSWORTH ESQ.

CHAPTER 17

JAMES RAMSDEN ESQ
Abbotswood 1867

Today I walked down from Abbotswood to my newly appointed railway siding. I was apprehensive at first, having my own private access to the very railway I helped to build, but then it is suitable for a Railway Director and first Mayor of Barrow-in-Furness. When I alighted on my return journey, I wandered into the hotel grounds, which houses the imposing abbey of Furness. The abbey is ancient and treasured by the local population, though they do not always treat it as they should, at times it becomes a veritable playground for the young urchins.

I had some issues in 1846 when we were first attempting to drive the new line through the valley. Rumours abounded that we were about to demolish the east end of the church. I admit, it was a fleeting thought, when we were trying to find an adequate solution. However, the disruption and difficulty which would have followed were not worth the distress. It was hard enough to discover a way to take the line through the valley; in the end our fine young engineer, Mr McClean, decided an extra £250 would be a useful investment to blow a tunnel through the hillside, thus preventing the line going too close to the east window of the abbey.

As I walked along the path behind the church, I recalled the feat of moving the river course and building a culvert beneath the line. The abbey looks as peaceful as it was before the railway was established. Trees are sparse on the hillside, but these will return in the future. It's a quiet place to sit and reflect on one's good fortune and each time a walk is taken one can see the skill of the ancient builders and one wonders about the exertions they must have endured without the benefit of modern tools and machinery.

Now that the navvies have left, the tranquillity has returned and the hotel which faces it has tamed the grounds. Our station is an opportunity to expand the business and develop the route to the Lake District. It is the gem in our crown and the accommodation is luxurious, attracting a better class of visitor. However, we also cater for the low classes, who mostly visit for the day with their numerous offspring. There is a pleasant second-class buffet next to the ticket office where food and drink can be taken at a reasonable cost. Many of the visitors are originally from places further afield and they are astonished to find such a huge and beautiful building to wander around. Of course, they are not permitted to enter the grounds through the hotel - that would not be acceptable; they must walk around the perimeter and then in through the paths. Some take the train back to town but many walk back to save their pennies.

James Ramsden

As I stroll around, I notice the new tennis courts between the ruins and the hotel. Further along I enter the abbey church and spot some young ladies walking down the night stairs, its precarious and I warn them to take care in their long dresses. The steps are almost worn away; it is not an edifying sight, for much of the ruins are like this, crumbling or overgrown. The groundsmen are taming the grass, trimming, and shaping so the lawns are greatly improved and enhance the red sandstone ruins. Gates have been placed across the opening to the grand room, which I believe was a Chapter House[89]; this allows them to be closed and locked at night.

We discovered tumbled masonry and disturbed grave covers during our work, and much was covered in ivy and was overgrown. Indeed, it did not look its best at that time, but the groundsmen have made a valiant effort at clearing it. The magnificent effigies have been removed from the open ground in the nave and taken into the little chapel at the end of the site. It has splendid, vaulted ceilings and offers some protection from the weather for these intricate statues.

It is fascinating to think of the masons who carved these likenesses and admire the technical skills they used. Even more exciting it is to muse upon who these faces are staring out from days gone by into our modern world of industry.

89 Chapter House - a daily meeting was held here, and a chapter read from the Rule of St Benedict

Were they wealthy patrons, of noble birth, like his Lordship the Duke? Or are they Templar knights returned from crusades in the Holy Land? Some indeed are religious, an abbot, a bishop or some such elite man of God. And the grand lady, coifed and demure, a knight's lady, a benefactor to the abbey, or some lady of import? We will never know. One passes from memory quickly as the years go by. I hope that I may be remembered; I and my "lady" perhaps replicated in the same sandstone, in the gothic manner in our new chapel at St George's church[90]. Our carved visages adorn the tracery around the altar in the chapel and our images will remain for as long as the church is sustained. Indeed, the chapel owes something to Furness Abbey. Its style is gothic and as grand as the church here would have been. A beautiful sedilia[91] mimicking the spectacular one here, graces the chapel, seats worthy of the town fathers, used in civic ceremonies as sober and important as the services in medieval times. One hopes it lasts as long, resplendent in red sandstone and slate, light drowning the church through the jewel like stained glass, just as in the medieval counterpart.

I notice the custodian, a grand fellow, not without intelligence. He looks smart in the livery of the Furness Railway and has an air of authority. He takes tours around the ruins and tells of the history and the tales of the past. I must bring my wife one Sunday; she would enjoy the experience I am sure. He has the benefit of a cottage at the end of the valley, where he and his family reside. We always care for our workers well. I have personally employed a butler, Patrick McGrory[92], and his family reside in a pleasant gatehouse at the end of my long drive.

My wander today has heartened me. I was correct to choose the hill above Furness Abbey for my mansion; it is a uniquely beautiful and impressive building. One wonders about the medieval abbots and the position they once held; they must have enjoyed a charmed life. The medieval potentates must be startled in their graves each time an engine rumbles past their towering edifice.

It seems most appropriate that I am now master of all I survey; I am truly lucky to have achieved so much in my life. I am sure my beautiful manor house compares well with the lodgings in which the old abbots lived. Abbotswood, an echo from the past, an equivalent residence as fit for my position as the abbot's house was for him. A very satisfying thought indeed.

I must now repair to my residence, for my wife will wonder where I am.

---

90 St George's church - the first church in Barrow, Anglican and the Civic church still used today
91 The Sedilia was an ornate carved row of seats used by the officiants during Mass
92 Patrick McGrory and family were registered on the 1881 Census

CHAPTER 18

HARPER GAYTHORPE - 1895

12 Harrison Street, Saturday, 14th Sept.

Barrow-in-Furness,

Lancashire.

To the Secretary,

St Mary of Furness

A Visit in 1895 by the Cumberland and Westmorland Antiquarian and Archaeological Society

It is with great pleasure that I can submit my report upon the recent visit to Furness Abbey by members and wives of the Cumberland and Westmorland Antiquarian and Archaeological Society (to be known hereafter as CWAAS for efficiency of words). Please find photographs and an account of the attendees, topics and discussions during this illustrious event. I hope that this report can be shared with the members in due course. It was an enjoyable day and with your kind permission I will share the photographs with the Barrow Naturalists' Society. As you know, I am a founder member of this society and Furness Abbey possesses a remarkably interesting array of flora and fauna throughout the site.

St Mary's Abbey of Furness has long been the central diamond in the diadem of the Furness Peninsula and one which I and others have researched. The visit was arranged to allow an educational tour for the members and their guests and was a grand opportunity to record this event by photography. This relatively new medium is excellent for capturing a single moment in time for posterity. I have established a small collection of these photographic memories and hope that in future they may be used by those historians who follow. It will be useful to see the buildings as they are now in 1895, but also to record that there are people who hold an academic and historical interest in the area. It always seemed strange to me that the rich heritage and environment of this corner of North West England is so little known. I can only hazard that this is because of its natural geographical isolation from the me populated parts of our nation. This is now being challenged by the progression of the railway and expands the area, connecting it with the larger part of the country. Indeed, some of our members travelled here by train for this convention, alighting at the charming Furness Abbey station. The irony of this being that although the monks sought seclusion, this abbey was always known, and its location verified. Otherwise, it might have escaped dissolution for much longer.

In my research about local legends, and folk lore I came across a most charming (yet erroneous) story about the final days of the abbey. Local folk, (and I mean indigenous inhabitants who hold ancestry here - unlike myself - being what locals term "an offcomer") tell the tale of the soldiers of Henry VIII being unable to find this abbey, being shrouded in remote woodland, until they heard the bells ringing for vespers. This of course, is a pure confection, built upon rumour and conjecture rather than solid evidence. The reality as you know, is very different, the abbey was never "lost" and all "roads" led to it.

Harper Gaythorpe, F. S. A. (Scot.)
President of the Barrow Naturalists' Field Club, 1902-3 and 1903-4.

The abbey provides us with great opportunities to investigate the ruins further and now that the site is governed by the Furness Railway Co. (with regards to the Duke of Devonshire of course), it becomes more accessible and a suitable destination for those visitors undertaking their own "grand tour" as it were. My friend WB Kendall has plans to investigate the site and I am sure that new information and artefacts will be uncovered.

Of course, we can look to other antiquarians for more information and historical context, and I would suggest CWAAS allow notification of such evidence to their members and maybe add some of these earlier sources to their archives. I am embarking upon the biography of one such scholar, Dr William Close of Dalton parish. Surprisingly, this man is little known beyond the immediate circle of academicians, yet his contributions to history, science and medicine, even music, are invaluable. He too, found great interest in Furness Abbey, which would have been in slightly better repair than today. Looking at the revisions he made to West's great work and the research papers which have been saved, show various walls and structures which no longer exist. This record is precious because we cannot otherwise know which buildings have disappeared latterly. I hope that my photographic evidence will contribute to this information and will inform future scholars and seekers of knowledge. It would appear that the historians eventually become part of the history they try to expound.

St Mary's of Furness is an incredibly significant part of the national historical picture too and we must ensure that it retains its position and importance even in its inevitable decline. (Here, I must indicate my concern that the railway running so closely beside the great east window is detrimental.) However, one cannot hold back the ravages of time and exploring lithographs and engravings (which in my opinion as a professional engraver are of a fine quality) indicates that the abbey is constantly altering and decaying. One can see why Turner sketched it on his tour of 1795, and again the changes are obvious. The current guardianship falls to the Cavendish family and, through their commercial interests, they have civilised the grounds somewhat.

The iron fencing protects the more vulnerable places, gated, and locked at night, with neatly laid pathways for easier perambulation of the location. Much of the intrusive vegetation has been removed and the red sandstone beneath can be better observed, revealing mason's marks, carvings, and the like.

There are several large trees which break into the ruins but enhance the view and provide shade from the sun on hot days. Several large tomb-covers and effigies are housed within the infirmary chapel, leaning against the walls in an intimidating fashion. There is scant evidence as to the identity of these characters, some decked as knights, one lady, high-born and some bland inscribed stones. We can guess or surmise as West and Beck did, but shall we ever really know who they were?

A dedicated custodian or guard has now been appointed to oversee the ingress and exit to the ruins, allowing some control of visitor numbers. This reduces the invasions of troublesome boys from the town who insist upon kicking a pig's bladder about in the cloister. He tells me on some summer days their number exceeds a hundred. This inevitably leads to climbing upon the monument and other ill-advised behaviour. I believe that this custodianship is the first of its kind in the country and is forward thinking of the guardians. He is smartly attired in a dark coloured uniform, with silver buttons, frock coat and cap. This gives him an air of authority and indeed, he does have a certain presence.

He has his own house at the south western end of the valley in a converted monastic building. The roof and roof timbers are original and are the only existing roofed building within the abbey complex. It has a ground floor and sleeping accommodation above, probably a later adaptation I would venture. This building must have been one of significance and was possibly an abbey water mill, being so close to the stream (which has been heavily engineered through the years). It is a charming setting for a home, rustic in appearance, ivy covered walls and fronted by a small garden.

One forgets, due to the lane bisecting the abbey grounds, that the whole valley was contained and inclusive within the boundary of the precinct walls, which are still visible in places. An archaeological survey would be most enlightening in this area of the abbey, I am sure.

I will lay off my idle musings for now and will look forward to hearing your comments on both the report and my photographs. I anticipate that these will form a salient collection for the future and hope that they endure long after I have expired and gone to meet my maker.

Yours faithfully,

Harper Gaythorpe Esq.

CHAPTER 19

BEATRIX POTTER VISITS THE ABBEY

Journal entry – 13th September 1900

Of course I had been to the Lake District before and loved it. As a family eight years ago, for our first visit, we rented Wray Castle on the shores of Lake Windermere where I met the Reverend Rawnsley[93], a most impressive man who has some fascinating ideas about the countryside there that have stayed with me. One day I would like to talk with him again about his plans.

It was also in the Lakes [as well as in Scotland] that my interest in drawing plants and studying fungi[94] developed further – the forest south of Hawkshead, the one called Grizedale - had many examples of the latter as well as the woods around Derwentwater where we had also stayed. We were keen on the fauna too: Bertram[95] and I used to try to tame some of the animals we came across so we could draw them in more details. Annie Carter[96], who was then our governess, encouraged us in this and I really imagined the creatures to have homes, families and even personalities of their own.

Then, four years ago we had a short holiday at Lakefield on the shores of Esthwaite Water and we often walked through the village of Near Sawrey. What a delightful place that is, with quaint cottages among the hills behind: it would be lovely to live there one day.

However, although we knew much of Lakeland I had never ventured this far south from Cumberland and Westmorland into the Low Furness part of Lancashire where we have come today. Father chose to visit the Abbey of Furness to photograph it[97], and I was delighted to accompany him, thinking I could draw while he was taking photographs.

---

93 Rev Hardwicke Rawnsley later founded the National Trust to whom Potter gave hundreds of acres of farmland on her death.

94 Three years earlier Potter had a paper, On the Germination of Spores, published but, as a woman, could not present it.

95 Bertram was Beatrix's younger brother

96 Annie later married and left the employ of the Potters but she and Beatrix remained friends.,

97 Her father, Rupert, was a keen and talented amateur photographer in the very early days of that pastime.

People have commented that it could be seen as strange that I, the younger generation, have chosen the older art whereas my father loves experimenting with the new. But Bertram is of the same opinion as myself that drawing allows more of the character of the artist to shine through and we have drawn ever since children. Indeed, he has encouraged my drawing and writing more than our parents.

So, back to today … we journeyed to the grounds of the abbey of the High Church of St Mary of Furness. It is certainly an enchanting place, the ancient ruins set in a tranquil valley with trees on two sides and a natural amphitheatre on a third; I heard that was once a pond here the monks fished! I had

Beatrix Potter by King

some drawing paper in front of me on my small easel and father had his tripod out a little distance away. Both of us were concentrating hard in our individual creative endeavours, endeavours made easier by the peace all around but, whereas papa looked up at the high walls of the ruins, I was looking down at the flowers, grasses and herbs around the edge of the abbey grounds. For what I intended to be a short break I walked up into the wood above the abbey where I was rewarded with many examples of my favourite plants, the fungi that were just starting to appear. I am fascinated by fungi and have studied mycology[98] a great deal of late. Sitting to draw them in close up, I lost track of time and discovered I had been up there for nearly two hours when I heard my father calling me. So I put away my equipment straightaway.

My father, bless him, has been such a help to me. Not only does he encourage me to accompany him on trips like this but he has introduced me to such worthy gentlemen as Sir John Everett Millais who was kind enough to praise my little sketches and encourage me to draw more. I have also been writing more of late. Indeed, the silly little story I included in a letter to Annie's son, Noel, some years ago has remained in my mind and this year I have been re-writing it for it may be considered worthy of publication one day, and then my four young rabbits, Flopsy, Mopsy, Cottontail and Peter could be in a real book for all children.[99]

Meanwhile, I made my way back down to the abbey where father was waiting to go and I was shocked to notice that the peace of that tranquil place had been shattered by a small group of urchins shouting and screaming as they ran around. So annoying. Children should surely be seen and not heard!

---

98 Mycology – the study of fungi

99 At first, *The Tale of Peter Rabbit* was printed just for the family but the following year Frederick Warne & Co agreed to publish the "bunny book".

CHAPTER 20

LADY DOROTHEA FANSHAWE - 1913

Lt. Gen H V Fanshawe

The Manor

Long Hanborough

Oxon

Furness Abbey Hotel

Barrow-in-Furness

Lancs

March 23rd 1913

Dear Hubert,

Elizabeth and I are enjoying our stay here and I think it is doing her the world of good being away from home and the thoughts of her loss. As her elder sister, I am content to play the role of comforter and confidante, putting aside my own needs for her sake. Losing her Edward to consumption[100] was, as you are aware, a great shock, even though he had been ill for some time, and her own mental fortitude was deteriorating during the period of mourning, and the legal arrangements afterwards. I feel this tranquil setting in a quiet valley is extremely beneficial for her, even if it has meant much extra work for myself.

The journey by train was long and quite tiresome as we had to change several times; it was clearly the correct decision to bring James as our porter and Mary as our handmaid – both have proved invaluable, for rail travel does take it out of one, you know. The final train of the journey, on the Furness Line, was the shortest and the most scenic with occasional glimpses of the Lakeland hills of which we had heard so much. It was, however, the least smooth of our trains and I am grateful we were not with the wretches in third class on their wooden benches.

---

100 Consumption was the old name for tuberculosis and a common, often fatal, disease at the time.

We alighted at the Furness Abbey station and fortunately, the hotel itself is both conveniently adjacent to the station and surprisingly luxurious. I am grateful to your connections with the Cavendishes[101] for arranging our stay with the railway company; we are due to meet them for luncheon tomorrow, our final day here; they are sending a carriage for us.

When we arrived it was a cool day with strong winds, although this "Vale of Nightshade" is fairly sheltered. Nevertheless, we did feel the chill and so, once I had organised James and Mary to see to the luggage and our rooms, Elizabeth and I sat by the roaring fire in the inglenook fireplace downstairs warming ourselves with a glass or two. It was so comfortable that I asked Mary to arrange with the hotel to reserve these chairs for us while we were here.

Our rooms too were pleasantly commodious; I confess to have rarely stayed in hotel rooms as suitable for a pair of middle-ages ladies. Dinners have also been more than acceptable, perhaps not as refined as we are used to at home where Alphonse produces his masterpieces, but for a hotel in the provinces it suits us perfectly. We have chosen to have our breakfasts in the conservatory which runs down the full side of the hotel facing the railway with the woods behind. Service is good with many well-turned out staff and, although I would have preferred the warmer dining room, Elizabeth prefers the lighter conservatory so I must, as ever, give way to her wishes.

For our first full day, as the winds had died and it remained dry, we had a walk around the ruins of Furness Abbey itself. We went through the custodian's gate by his hut and he was very informative, if rather officious. I did have to remind him who he was talking to but it hardly affected his manner and tone. I have to say the ruins are particularly impressive and the carvings in the red sandstone were fascinating. Elizabeth loved sitting in the cloisters looking at the five arches; she has always been the more imaginative member of the family and I feel she was thinking of the life of the monks here some five hundred years before. I left her there for a while as I wandered off to organise James to fetch my chair and a decanter of gin – I am acquiring a taste for this more and more these days. I must have dozed off for I was woken by Elizabeth who was having one of her turns, so sisterly duties came first once more.

Yesterday we had a rather exciting excursion. The hotel organises tours of some of the lakes further north in Cumberland and we ordered a carriage, booked tickets ahead and set off. It was a long day but we had a good stop for lunch at a

---

101 The Cavendish family did (and still do) own the land on which the Abbey stands and the hotel stood.

hostelry by the side of Windermere and, the highlight of the day, a trip on two steamboats, the first from Lakeside on the southern end of Windermere up the length of the lake in the morning. Then, after lunch and a journey in a coach and four around the top of the two lakes, we boarded a beautiful boat on Coniston Water called the Gondola [it actually does resemble the Venetian craft] to sail south again. I must tell you, Herbert, that I have not seen such beautiful scenery since our Swiss holiday three years ago. I had not realised England contained such a magnificent landscape.

Although it was a day trip not to have been missed, it was rather tiring and I think I can speak for both of us when I say we were pleased to get back to the Abbey Hotel and sink into the chairs by the inglenook with another glass or two before dinner. I did have a break and wandered a little to watch two gentlemen playing billiards, such a curious game.

Elizabeth has told me she would like to draw in the abbey grounds in the morning before we go to Holker – I hope she does not require my presence for I feel I will need to rest.

Well, my dear Hubert, that is my account of our time in the north. How are things in the Home Counties? Are you still busy with your meetings with the politicians and other military men? And how are the twins? Tell them I miss them but am proud that they have decided to sign up for the army in October; I am sure all this talk of Germany will come to nothing and they will enjoy the army life as much as you have done.

We should be home in two days' time, assuming the trains run well.

Your loving wife,

CHAPTER 21

CORPORAL BOB AINSWORTH - 1941
Barrow Air Defence Hq

May 2nd 1941

To my beloved Mary,

If you receive this from someone else other than me, it will mean I have been killed.

As you know there has been German bombing over Barrow for some nights now. The Luftwaffe are obviously targeting the Vickers shipyard but they know, I think, that we co-ordinate the town's air defences from here at the Abbey Hotel which we requisitioned last year. So, I would not be surprised if they also targeted us. With a railway station next door to us, it is inevitable in my humble opinion.

When it was decided to base the town's anti-aircraft headquarters here, it was thought being in a partly wooded valley would hide it from the enemy aircraft. Since I cannot be punished if the censors see this, as I will be dead, I can tell you that was a stupid notion. It may be secluded from the ground but it is clearly visible from the air. Indeed, when the Hindenberg passed over Barrow[102] five years ago they could well have been taking photographs of the whole area. They know we're here.

Because of my polio I am able to do only administrative jobs around the place but it does enable me to observe a lot of what goes on. I am not as dim as many here think I am and I can see errors being made both in communications and decisions made. But, naturally, I say nothing. I wander the abbey grounds when off-duty and wonder if Hitler is going to finish what Henry VIII started. I do hope not: it's a magical place that affects everyone. Even big Les goes a little quieter when he's by the abbey, it's the effect this place has on folk.

---

102 On May 23rd 1936 the Hindenberg airship was seen flying low over Barrow, its swastika clearly visible.

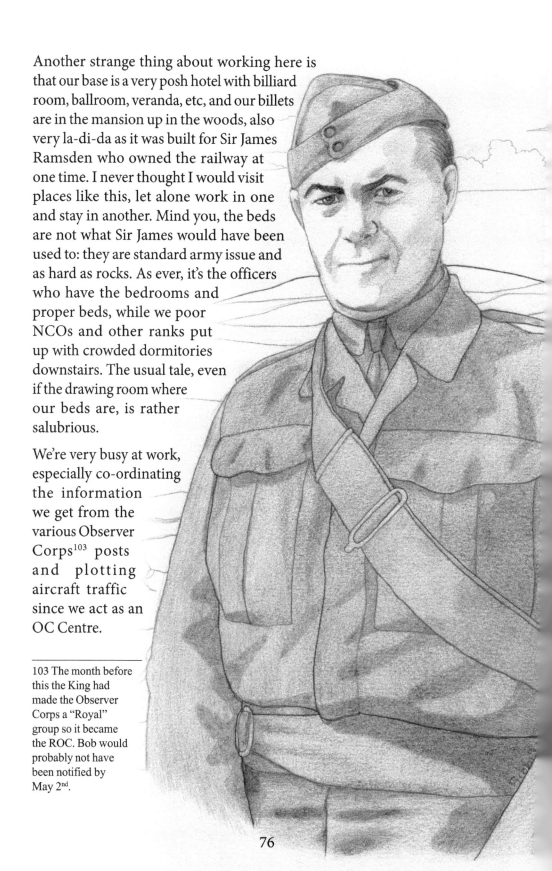

Another strange thing about working here is that our base is a very posh hotel with billiard room, ballroom, veranda, etc, and our billets are in the mansion up in the woods, also very la-di-da as it was built for Sir James Ramsden who owned the railway at one time. I never thought I would visit places like this, let alone work in one and stay in another. Mind you, the beds are not what Sir James would have been used to: they are standard army issue and as hard as rocks. As ever, it's the officers who have the bedrooms and proper beds, while we poor NCOs and other ranks put up with crowded dormitories downstairs. The usual tale, even if the drawing room where our beds are, is rather salubrious.

We're very busy at work, especially co-ordinating the information we get from the various Observer Corps[103] posts and plotting aircraft traffic since we act as an OC Centre.

_____

103 The month before this the King had made the Observer Corps a "Royal" group so it became the ROC. Bob would probably not have been notified by May 2nd.

As you know, I am a Teller [104] and have a group of OC posts to administer so I collect their telephone reports and add them to a written report to pass on. Lately, the reports have been coming through thick and fast so there are times when we are rushed off our feet to make sure RAF Fighter Command bases, searchlight bases and anti-aircraft batteries are aware of what's going on. But there are quiet times too when we stare at the phones wanting them to ring to break the boredom; it's mad busy or nothing here.

However, things have hotted up so much in the last week that we expect a big attack any time now. The bombing that Barrow has suffered so far is, I'm afraid, just the beginning. We're expecting a huge wave very soon. And, going by what has happened so far, the accuracy of the bombing may mean it's not just their primary targets that are hit but lots of areas of the town. I fear for, not just myself, but all those that live nearby. Last month the Waverley Hotel and a couple of churches[105] along with much of Abbey Road were destroyed and they were not military targets.

I am so pleased you are not in Barrow, dear Mary, and I pray this letter never reaches you[106] and that I return to your loving arms when I next have leave so that we can plan our wedding for later this year.

I must go now, my love, as I am on duty tonight and I need some rest.

Look after yourself and remember that I love you.

Your fiancé,

Bob

---

104 A Teller was responsible to liaising with local OC posts, etc, as Bob says.
105 Christ Church and the Abbey Road Baptist church
106 Sadly, the letter did reach Mary with its sad message. The hotel and station were badly damaged in the bombing and never used again. The hotel was demolished (apart from the ticket office which became a tavern) in 1951-3.

CHAPTER 22

FURNESS ABBEY MYSTERY/PASSION PLAYS[107] 1958-88
Interviews with those who took part

1. Walter Johnston

How nice to meet you – do come in. Have a seat over there and we can start chatting. You want to know about my connection with the Mystery plays? Yes, well, let me think: it started back in the 1950s when I was doing acting and voice work. I've been blessed with a strong voice and, when I was young, I was tall and, people said, had a presence on stage. At the time of the first Abbey Mystery play in July **1958** I was training for the theatre under Margaret Rudd and Barbara Wrigley, a voice coach who taught at the Blackwell School on Windermere.[108]

The Reverend W A Batty, vicar of St Matthew's church in Barrow, adapted the play and Phillip Bromley produced it, while Stuart Lawrence directed and played the part of Christ. I was invited to play in the speaking chorus, as an attendant to Pharaoh [that's me on the right below] and as a silent Angel Michael – I remember having to carry a huge sword. Quite a few of us had to play several of the smaller parts – we didn't mind that at all, it was part of being an actor. Moreover, the audience had to be barefoot so some things were worse for them.

We used the east window as Heaven with blue velvet backing and a huge brass star whereas Hell was at the Norman doorway disguised by a horrifying representation of its mouth [see below]. A donkey was hired, collected from the railway station and walked to the abbey. Pigeons to represent doves were collected daily from Marsh Street, Barrow.

---

107 Mystery plays in the Middle Ages were often performed by trades guilds and were based on bible stories. Before any theatres were built these were the only plays allowed and the ones at Chester, York, Coventry and Wakefield were the most well-known.
108 Now the Blackwell Arts and Crafts Centre

Mystery Play

During the scene of the cleansing of the temple they were released where they made a magnificent sight as they flew over the abbey and back home - unless they decided to roost and had to be coaxed out one by one to the annoyance of the owner. Although the plays were organised by the churches, local dramatic and musical societies took part, with ordinary folk playing other citizens.

Another important, indeed imposing person then, whom I must not omit to mention is Edith Eckersley who had the music shop by the Ritz cinema in Barrow and one in Ulverston; she also founded the Ulverston Outsiders. As if this wasn't enough, she was the church organist at St Mary's on Walney and lived on Abbey Road. Her influence on the plays cannot be overestimated, especially on the musical side.

The great Millom poet, Norman Nicholson, wrote the introduction in the programme I have here, saying that "the performance of the Mystery Plays at Furness Abbey belongs ... to a long and honourable tradition. For, in seeing these street-corner masterpieces, we will be able not only to watch the whole scope of Man's redemption from the Creation to the Last Judgement, as seen through medieval eyes, but also to relive one of the great religious experiences of Christendom." In a later programme he added, "the production to be seen at Furness Abbey will be very different from the annual performances given in the late Middle Ages. At the Abbey the performances will be presented reverently and with much skill and foresight. Music, costume, lighting and the solemn and romantic setting of the ruins will combine to work on the imagination." And he was right, you know, we did depend on the audience to use their imagination. I hope they did.

****

Three years later, in **1961**, my reputation had increased and so did my part in the plays. This time, as well as the chorus, I played the part of Lazarus. The director was Canon W J Bucks and the producer was again Phillip Bromley who had been the director of the White Rose Players in York. Through him I met the famous ballet director, Helen May, who asked me to perform in the matinée. Phillip Bromley then called on me at home in Greengate Street and asked me the join the White Rose players. I was even introduced to a tall man who turned out to be Ken Russell, the great film director, who asked me to get in touch if I wanted a role in a repertory theatre..

Anyway, back to the Mystery Play at Furness Abbey – you must forgive an old man digressing.

I remember just a few things from that year. I do remember that the north window of the abbey was Heaven so people could look upwards, and there was an amusing moment when someone slipped over and said aloud, "Oh Christ!". At that someone else shouted, "He's not on till Act Two!"

I also recall that the actress playing Mary, mother of Jesus, was the daughter of the vicar of St Luke's church. She came in on a donkey we had borrowed from Manor Farm. For the birth of baby Jesus, she had a doll up her skirt. At the dramatic moment, she lifted her skirt and, just as the "baby" appeared, the donkey decided to relieve himself right next to a microphone. To the audience it sounded like a waterfall and created quite a stir.

So we did have some amusing moments, although the plays were serious.

****

The next Furness Abbey Mystery play was five years later, in **1966**. This time there were seven performances, increasing from just three in 1958.

And I was promoted again … if having the part of Satan could be called promotion! I wore a black leotard with red and green designs and had to slither like a snake across the grounds into the mouth of hell! I still have that leotard somewhere … oh, here it is, rather creased, I'm afraid, but it does remind me of that production. I was even mentioned in the review of the play in the Manchester Guardian which praised my "speaking voice, tone and musicality." Indeed, I have always loved the music of the spoken word, especially with the alliteration in medieval writing that gives it a special sound.

Some of the rehearsals took place in my house in Barrow and, although Graham Souter was the producer, the man who impressed me most was Cyril Dent, his assistant, a brilliant man who really knew his stuff.

I have kept lots of material from the plays: scripts, photographs, programmes, letters and press cuttings. Although I am an old man in his mid-eighties now, I remember those plays with fondness and surprising clarity. Good times.

Oh, look at the time. I know you have to go. I do hope I have been of some help to you. Goodbye.

2. John Twyford

Thank you for asking me about the **1988** Mystery Plays at the Abbey. I'm not sure I can remember a lot, but I'll do my best to put my thoughts down for you.

I do recall that we principals met in the Abbey Tavern before and after the show. Several professionals were in the cast: I especially remember Richard Franklin of Doctor Who fame. The director, David Marcus, really went to town on the show. He invited Prince Edward and was so proud that he accepted; he flew in and so security was tight with a restricted number of tickets and dogs everywhere. Melvyn Bragg was there too. David also arranged for the BBC to put on a re-enactment of the Furness Abbey monks crossing Morecambe Bay from Canal Foot via

Mystery Play

Chapel Island to Flookburgh. Several cast members including myself took part and we were led by the Queen's sand pilot, Cedric Robinson. With his silver hair and angelic features Cedric looked wonderful in his monk's cowl.

I played High Priest Caiaphas and Iain Nicholson, as the second priest, started referring to me as Number One. Soon the rest of my brethren started to give themselves numbers and on the opening night I arrived in the dressing tent to a chorus of "evening, number seven", "how are you, number six?"; "has number four arrived yet?" Forget priests, we sounded like a chorus of dastardly Bond villains! I seem to remember that at some point there was a football match, priests v disciples in the amphitheatre. But the memories are vague. Oh, and Jeff Olsted from Radio Cumbria was the Voice of God projecting down from the highest tower – quite effective that was.

Our leading man, Peter Duncan, ex-Blue Peter presenter, who played Jesus, got on well with everyone and was very approachable. I remember he and I had a lengthy discussion on how to play our scene towards the climax of the show. Peter suggested we should tone everything down and make it more intimate, while I, bearing in mind the size of the Abbey favoured a more traditional delivery. Curiously on the night, without even intending to, I took my performance down a little and Peter lifted his. Of course, thinking back Peter was quite right, especially as we had throat mikes and there was no real need for a great deal of vocal projection.

One performance had to be cancelled half-way through because of the pouring rain: that was the show where the donkey flatly refused to move, causing rather inappropriate laughter that spoiled the sombre moment.

The most controversial thing about the production concerned the portrayal of Adam and Eve. As far as I remember it was Malcolm Smith who was to appear as natural as possible with just the traditional fig leaf to preserve his modesty and the actress playing Eve was to wear a body stocking or possibly go topless. Anyway word got out and a photographer from the Sun newspaper arrived to take some pictures of one of the performances. There were many children in the cast and some of the parents were not happy with this arrangement, so director David decided that the actors would cover up. A rather disgruntled Sun photographer left with no page 3. Serves him right!

Nevertheless, the audience loved the shows and promenading. Comments we received included: "magical", "utterly spectacular", "moved me to tears".

Anyway, is that okay? I do wish I could remember more. [109]

---

109 Although Walter and John gave most of the content here, I have added bits from other people too.

CHAPTER 23

ROOSE COUNTY PRIMARY SCHOOL PUPIL, AGED 10
"My Trip to Furness Abbey" - Tuesday, 11th July 1967

Class 4 had our school trip today. We were all dead excited because we were going to Furness Abbey. Our teachers, Mr Marshall and Mr Andrews, told us to bring a packed lunch in a bag and to wear sensible shoes; we had to have a packamac too just in case the weather broke. It was lucky that the weather was sunny and warm and we set off from school at 9 o'clock. We had to walk in pairs; I walked with my best friend and we had to hold hands. We walked right past my house and I waved to my sister who was in the garden. When we came to the end of the houses we were in the lane. It was quiet, apart from the sheep baa-ing and the birds singing. The hedges were full of dog roses and cow parsley and there were lots of bees. It was a long way to the abbey and my feet were hurting when we got there where my shoes had rubbed. We had to wait in line until Mr Marshall had talked to the man in the ticket office.

I really like that little house; it looks like a cottage from a story. The man has a uniform and cap like a policeman. He leans over the door (it's split in half) and counts your money on the ledge and gives you a ticket from his machine. On cold days he has a little fire in there and you see the smoke coming out of the chimney.

I like the abbey. We sometimes go there on our Sunday walks after dinner. It's really old and looks like a castle, but it's not - it's where the monks used to live. Monks are like vicars, but they don't get married, and they pray a lot.

Mr Marshall told us to put our bags by the wall and we could get them later for our packed lunch. Everybody did as they were told because he can be a bit scary if people are naughty. We all had to follow him so he could tell us all about the abbey (he knows everything). He told us that where we left our bags was a cloister, but we had to use our imagination because there is only one wall left. He showed us two massive bookcases (they are like tunnels in the walls) we could go in and we all made our voices echo. I wondered where the bookshelves went. We walked through an archway into a room with six fancy pillars. Mr Marshall said this was where the monks met every day and where some of the abbots were buried. It's strange burying people inside a room, I think.

In the church we could see the altar and there were some special seats, with fancy carving. Mr Marshall said it was called a sedilia. There were some funny stairs that stopped halfway up the wall. The bottom steps had been taken away because they were so badly worn. He called them the night stairs and said that the monks slept up there in "dormitories" and had to come into church in the middle of the night to pray. I don't think I would have liked to be a monk. I have been up those stairs. My dad lifted me up so I could see what was up there once. It would be much easier if the steps went all the way to the floor! Mr Marshall said I would have been in trouble if the ticket man had seen me.

We went back to the cloister and sat on the grass with our packed lunches. It was nice sitting in the sun. I had egg sandwiches and a can of fizzy pop. It took me ages to drink it all so I could put the can in my bag. Everyone made sure they picked up their rubbish and put it in their bag to take it home.

After lunch we went to the river; Mr Marshall told us that this was the toilet for the monks and that everything fell into the water to be washed away. We all pulled a face when he said the river ran from there to the kitchen. Yuck! Then he said we could have a play if we didn't go in the river or climb over any fences. He thinks we can be trusted because we are ten now and

know how to behave. He must have forgotten what some of the boys are like because four of them did go in the beck and got wet feet. We didn't tell though because the teachers looked so comfortable sitting on the grass. My friend Christine and I went exploring. There was a graveyard with some stone coffins, some of the others laid down in them to see how big they were. We played there for ages. Some of us went up the slope to a building that had a huge tunnel underneath it. You could see right to the other end, but it did look a long way. We had to bend down to go in and it was a bit wet in there, but we managed to crawl all the way to the other end. It was good fun, so we crawled all the way back again too.

Next, we went to the kitchen; it was an octagon shape and it had a sink and a rubbish chute. Mr Marshall said the monks threw their rubbish into the river down there. We all looked over the little ledge to see if there was any rubbish in the water. At 3 o'clock the whistle went and we had to meet at the cloister. We got in our pairs and set off home. When we got back to school, we were tired and got there just in time for the bell to ring. It was a great school trip I would like to go again.

If I grow up and become a teacher, I will take my class to the abbey every single year. It's brilliant.

****

Mrs J. - Teacher

Report of School Trip to Furness Abbey 2000

Class 4 had their annual visit to Furness Abbey as part of the history curriculum studying a historical site significant to their locality. We had pre-booked through English Heritage and advised them of our arrangements.

We walked from Victoria Infants School to Furness Abbey in pairs, accompanied by staff/adults to a ratio 1-4. We had a designated first aider and emergency phone and had left trip details in the school office.

Mrs Helm lead the class and I followed. We arrived at ten o'clock just as the visitor centre opened. We left our bags with packed lunches in the Education room and visited the facilities before we set off on our tour of the ruins. The children dressed in monks' habits to walk around and try to "become" monks for the day. They were given clip boards with their questionnaires and pencils and were asked to complete these as we walked around. We started at the guest house and everyone was excited to find mason's marks - we discovered a carved fish and a cross. The groundsman, Tom, was there, and he kindly showed us the carving of Nine Men's Morris on the doorstep.

We carried on into the church and sketched the sedilia, some people finished their picture quickly and Garry had to be stopped from lifting Ryan up onto the night stairs. We moved to the quire stalls and split into two groups and pretended to be monks, standing silently for a minute. We managed twenty seconds before Laura and Emily wanted to go to the toilet and Luke and Garry started sniggering. The children ran into the bell tower and piled around the gated doorway. Most of them were convinced this was a prison and would not accept any other explanation.

In the cloister we measured the dimensions by walking the perimeter-slowly like monks. It started well but ended like a race as everyone wanted to reach the book cupboards first. It's quite amazing that you can fit thirty children (and two dads) in there and makes you wonder how many books they held. We were looking at the vaulting in the vestibule to the Chapter House, but this was disturbed by Thomas and Luke scuffling their shoes in the gravel. We had just entered the Chapter House when William screamed. He had been stung by a wasp. Miss Allison took him to have first aid and then Freya and Georgia wanted to go to the toilet.

We all went to the reredorter - this caused much mirth, and everyone looked for the remains of monkish excrement in the stream. The whole class was disgusted and fascinated in equal measure when they realised the water ran into the kitchen. William and the two girls returned. We went to the infirmary next, and the children tried to sing like monks in the chapel so they could hear the echo. This became quite rowdy, and we had to calm down. Then Jessica was stung by another wasp.

We pressed on to the abbot's house and we impressed on the children that under no circumstances should they crawl through the tunnel beneath. Mrs Helm had to shout at the two dads who were half-way through!

We broke for lunch and sat on the steps of the visitor centre. After lunch, the children went off in groups with an adult and collected the final answers for their quiz.

We had difficulty hauling Luke and Garry out of the stream and we had to wring out their habits. Everyone had brought a pound for the shop - except everyone hadn't! The children threaded in and out of the shelves, picking up pencils, toys and books, many of which cost more than £1, moving like hyenas after their prey. This caused problems and the Chancellor of the Exchequer would have had problems balancing the books with the array of objects and heaps of various coins planted on the counter. The lady was very patient considering and looked relieved as we left to queue outside. The teachers were all out of pocket by the end, having made up the shortfall.

It was an experience reprising my school trip to the abbey, but both were fun and introduced the children to an amazing artefact on their doorstep. Let's hope they remember and keep this place in their hearts forever.

(Any resemblance to people living or dead is purely coincidental!)

CHAPTER 24

NATE JEPSON
Archaeologist - 2010

Growing up in the Furness area, there was always an abundance of things to do. The Lake District is on our doorstep and the sea surrounds the peninsula giving us a fantastic but dangerous tidal bay, a pebble filled beach which is always windy from the Irish Sea, and grass topped sand dunes. But there is one place that we visited as kids again and again. Furness Abbey.

Set in a hidden valley, between Dalton and Barrow stands Furness Abbey, the large red sandstone Cistercian Abbey built in 1127. I remember visiting the abbey so many times as a kid, that I could tell you all the hiding places, all the little nooks and crannies that only a child could hide in. There were drains that were dotted around and barred up for safety, that my friend got his leg stuck in, and the tunnels where the water would run. It's a quiet tranquil place that I have been tied to since I was a young kid.

Nate Jepson

Childhood

Running to the first patch of stones, which I now know to be the stable block, my elder brother and I would race to be the first one to find the fish shaped mason's mark. We would then go to the cemetery gatehouse which had a small but exciting spiral staircase that we could climb up and see over the top, (now my own sons love this too). We would run around, play, and even have picnics at the abbey. On a particularly nice days, we would stay there all day.

Archaeology

I got the archaeology bug young and dreamed of being Indiana Jones but never thought I would dig at the abbey. Eventually I became an archaeologist travelling up and down the country digging on many exciting sites. I dug Roman, Iron Age sites, and even travelled up to Scotland to survey a Pictish settlement. But one of my better memories comes from having the unique opportunity to excavate around the presbytery of Furness Abbey. Being given permission to dig on an English Heritage site was exciting and rare. We knew from the historical record that much had already been excavated by the Victorians long before we arrived. But it was exciting none the less.

The Road to Piel

In 2009 I was placed on a watching brief, which meant I had to watch a mechanical digger excavate a path near the abbey, in preparation for a new cycle path. If anything interesting turned up, I'd halt the job and excavate by hand to preserve any archaeology. It's an extremely popular path today and is used all the time. I like to say I built it! I didn't but it was my job. We were coming to the end, literally only 5-10m of path left, when the mechanical digger pulled up a large rock. And then another. And then another. I stopped the job and began digging.

It turned out I'd just discovered an old road that appeared to be leading towards the abbey. It was cobbled and had a lot of wheel ruts at the edges. It was a well-used road and within the fill I discovered several pottery shards that dated the road back to 1600s. As I only excavated where the path runs, that section is now covered, but it was interesting to see if the road continued. Using a long metal spike, I poked the ground and, yes, there was the sound of the road continuing. It continued towards the amphitheatre, where I believe it led up the hill to another patch of road that can be seen further up the new cycle path. A local historian, Alice Leach, came to see what had been found and was so excited she brought the Evening Mail down to photograph it.

The Presbytery

We[110] were asked to assist in trying to fix the presbytery as numerous cracks had appeared, and it was feared it was dangerous and could fall. Being a Grade 1 scheduled site, before any repairs could be done archaeologists had to dig down inside and outside of the presbytery to the footings and record anything we found. According to the historical record, oak floats supported the sandstone blocks of the building. We had to dig down to ascertain whether the wood had started to break or rot, so that we could see where the damage was coming from.

I had the pleasure of digging both inside the presbytery and outside. I dug outside hoping that there would be the possibility of some human remains in the cemetery, but alas, they had all been removed, or at least there were none where I had dug. I traced a large crack right down to the oak float, which was well over six foot from the current ground level.

Inside the Presbytery

When I was digging inside the presbytery down to a low level I happened to find a sandstone block formation about one or two metres from the end of the existing straight presbytery wall. It was odd, as it was a perfect semi-circle that connected to two other runs of stone. It turned out that I had found the curved apse end of the original Romanesque church. This predated what stands there today and was part of the original Savigniac church. For me, this was a great experience and something that I will always remember.

The Abbot

One day one of my colleagues was digging a little way away from where I was, and he called us all over with disbelief in his voice. We all huddled round and as we watched him dig carefully, something white appeared in the reddish fill. We realised that he was slowly revealing the skull of what would become the full skeleton of an abbot from the abbey. The remarkable thing is, up until that point, everything we were excavating was old stone coffins, one that read, Adam De Grisholm[111] (Greenhaume), and other back fill from the Victorian excavations. But this skeleton had been completely missed and was extremely exciting. It had lain undisturbed throughout those excavations, only to be found by us.

---

110 Oxford Archaeology North

111 Adam de Grisholm was a local landowner and donor to the abbey. His tomb cover is recorded in West's Antiquities of Furness, which means it was removed and used as backfill some time after 1744, possibly during the Victorian excavations

However, that wasn't the most interesting thing. In his arms were the remains of a wooden staff. Most of the wood had crumbled away, but there was enough to see its shadow. At the top there appeared a golden crosier which, when we got it out of the ground, we looked closely and saw that it showed St Michael fighting a dragon. That wasn't all. On his finger was a ring, still in situ. The ring, when removed had a point on the underside[112] which would have been painful[113] to the wearer.

It was an staggering find, and a great experience to be a part of. I have visited the site several times since, seeing the crosier in pride of place at the museum. It's amazing, and what makes it even more amazing is that it wasn't discovered for so many years. It is gratifying to think that I was part of that discovery and I love being able to show it to my young sons, who are the next generation of my family to love Furness Abbey.

---

112 Bezel
113 For penance and mortification to remind him of his "opus dei" or duty to God

CHAPTER 25

FURNESS ABBEY FELLOWSHIP 2012 onwards

Leeann Herbert

Furness Abbey Fellowship started when the first group of interested people met in the back room of the Red Lion at Dalton in the spring of 2012. From that original meeting myself and the tenacious Gill Jepson are the only remaining originals. However, I need to give a special mention to the late Alice Leach who came along and inspired the group. But all those there attended due to their personal interest and love for the local abbey. Also, up until January 2020 Vanessa Allen was one of the longest serving members, as well as being active in the Barrow Civil History Society where she is Chair. I fell into the role of FAF Secretary because I was organised enough to take a note book and pen and Gill couldn't multi-task (talk and note take simultaneously).

Another interested group, The Iron Shepherds, were also part of the original group and, although Stuart Appley stepped back due to personal commitments, we still have close links and the group's medieval re-enactments are a highlight at our fairs [see later] each year.

At that original meeting the group discussed their interest in the abbey and attracting more people to visit. We really had no idea of what we wanted to do or how to achieve whatever it was: we just wanted to be involved in the abbey and its future. Within a few meetings a more active group emerged that began to work on the long term actions of the group. Our original mission statement has hardly changed: '*Furness Abbey Fellowship is a group that has been formed to support English Heritage, taking on the role of a critical friend. The group intends to support restoration of the Abbey and wishes to increase access to its facilities. The group also desires to aid the development of the Abbey Museum by improving the visitors' experience.*'

Our ever present Chair (Gill Jepson) networked like crazy and through her many connections to the history groups in the area she attracted like-minded souls to join us. Gill worked hard on making a connection with English Heritage and eventually we had our first meeting with Clea Warner who kindly listened and advised how our group could become involved in supporting the work of E.H. and the abbey.

After a lot of hard work and determination from Gill, along with her passion for the abbey, the group began to develop its charitable status, mission statement and purpose. This supported our initial project to retain in the Abbey museum the fantastic crosier and staff of the Abbot found interned when the conservation was being carried out (see Chapter 25). This project developed from the need to fund a special display case for the artefacts to be preserved and displayed.

Therefore, the fundraising ideas began and the idea of a **Medieval Fair** was conceived and we eventually raised the £6000 needed for the special display case.

The aim of the first fair in 2013 was to raise the profile of the abbey, increase visitor numbers and predominantly raise funds for the case. We had our target and, although we did not know how long it would take us to reach it, we had a starting point. Local businesses, crafters, sponsors and artisans were sought, very much by Gill and any other connections the group had with others that would be interested in attending and being a part of the fair. The group also learned a lot about the management and strict protocols that are very much a part of any plans to hold a fair to EH's standard.

All our endeavours paid off: the first fair was a great success and the support from locals surpassed our expectations. Our invited patron, Lord Cavendish, paid a visit and has done so several times since. Again, through networking with other groups, we gained support from the Keswick to Barrow run committee, not only on a practical level on the day of the fair, but also through a substantial donation to FAF towards the display case costs. Certainly Gill's persistence and determination to have the crosier back at the abbey also encouraged E.H. to match the funds we raised, and this secured the display case and backdrop information that are now in the museum.

The name Furness Abbey Fellowship honestly started as tongue in cheek suggestion from myself and a little inspired by the famous Tolkein books; we were an eclectic little group, and came from quite diverse backgrounds. However, the name was approved and here we are; some might say that the nickname FAF or FAFfers or FAFfing around very much suits some of us! Well, that's my humble opinion and I cannot imagine the group being known by any other name.

We as a group have met in many places over the years and have been greatly supported by Jackie at The Abbey Mill Cafe and I think we have a firm friend in Lucy Ronald, the site manager. Through my friendship with everyone in the group I have been part of something fantastic and hopefully we will get back there again. I have picked up on the history of the abbey and its influence on the local and wider area. All down to many meetings, many long walks and hours with guess who....Gill.

****

Liz Critchley

I first met Gill and Leeann through my role at the Dock Museum. They came to see the 'famous' Rampside sword, a Viking piece donated to the museum. I had taken them into the collection stores to see the sword but as we passed by other objects from the collection, animated and detailed discussions were sparked. We chatted about both provenance and local history as the objects in the collection inspired and led our conversations and the visit was longer than planned and continued to cake and coffee! We struck up a friendship from there with a connection made on love of local history and an equal fondness for cake too!

I joined the Fellowship in 2012, initially as a representative from the museum; I moved onto work for the National Trust but continued as a member of FAF and am now the Treasurer.

I was part of the first Medieval Fair and my recollections are mainly doing a lot of walking around the site; my mum came along too as a volunteer but we wore her out by midday! We FAF members wore white t-shirts so we could recognise each other and visitors knew who we were. The meet and greet was on pop up tables facing the museum and manned with a fearsome crowd of wonderful volunteers entertaining visitors and raising funds through quizzes, face painting, crafts, books and FAF membership sales.

That first year we started with some of the participants that have continued every Fair since: our friends, The Iron Shepherds, who put on authentic re-enactments of medieval life, Patrick Corbett's showing the illuminated writing techniques that the monks used, Iain McNicoll as Brother John demonstrating the uses of herbs and the Dorian Players playing early Tudor music. We also had a hog roast and Abbey Mill providing other refreshments.

Leean Herbert and Liz Critchley

It was great to see the abbey alive with people from the local community supporting the return of the crosier and engaging with the place in such a tangible level.

Since then we have had a Medieval Fair almost every year, often in excellent weather; sadly in 2019 the winds were so strong we could not erect the marquees and safety instructions made us cancel, and then in 2020, Coronavirus forced us to cancel again. But we came back stronger than ever in 2021.

We may no longer need to raise money for keeping the crosier at the abbey, our greatest success, but we have other plans to raise money for improved signage, etc. to make our abbey even more attractive to visitors.

CHAPTER 26

OBITUARY OF ALICE LEACH -2014
"Historian Leaves Legacy of Learning and Love of the Past"

Alice Leach was a well-known local author and historian who sadly died in January. She was born in 1929 in Barrow-in-Furness and was immensely proud of her town. She was educated at Our Lady's School, Crosslands Convent and her faith was important throughout her life.

She went on to teach and during her career she endowed her pupils with her love of history and literature. She was creative in her approach and inspired the pupils to take pride in the heritage of her town just as she did. In the early 1980s she wrote a series of books called *Our Barrow* whilst being Head of History at Alfred Barrow School. She involved her pupils in the illustrations and some of the interpretation which was a unique approach in those days.

One of her pupils, Kay Thornton, who now lives in Canada, remembers her fondly. She met Alice in her first year at the school; she was the librarian and history teacher then. Kay tells of her abiding love of Furness Abbey and how Mrs Leach transformed the school playground into "a representation of Furness Abbey with pupils dressed in robes of Cistercian monks." This approach was successful and mirrored Mrs Leach's passion for the abbey. Kay goes on to say, "she had an insatiable love for the Abbey and local history which rubbed off on me."

Vanessa Allen, the current Chair of the Civic Society explains: "Alice was one of the founding members of Barrow Civic and Local History Society in 1985. She took on the role of Secretary and soon also the role of Chairperson. She organised the programme of lectures, guided walks, and tours, both at home and abroad. She became the driving force of the society and campaigned tirelessly to promote the town's Victorian heritage." Her energy and enthusiasm never depleted, and she was helpful in encouraging the initiation of Furness Abbey

Fellowship in 2012. Alice was Chairperson and Secretary of Barrow Civic and Local History Society for twenty-nine years.

Alice wrote numerous books about local history, particularly Furness Abbey; her seminal work was *A History of Furness Abbey*, published in 1987. Her research was meticulous, and she garnered admiration and acknowledgement from other historians such as Dr William Rollinson who wrote, "This book will delight and fascinate all those interested in Furness and Furness Abbey and Mrs Alice Leach should be congratulated on its production". He concluded that, "The book fills a gap in the literature of Furness Abbey," and he hoped, "it would be widely read", which of course it has been.

Alice herself wrote, "I have tried to present accurate information in a readable, interesting format …. for a wide readership…. for teachers and their pupils, as well as for the abbey's many visitors from home AND abroad…..in fact for all lovers of FURNESS ABBEY."

She was always interested in extending her knowledge of the Abbey and Kay Thornton remembers, "being reintroduced to her through my own research on Abbotswood and taking on an active part on the committee of the local Historic Society whose chairman was Alice Leach."

Mrs Leach was also heavily involved in the Mystery Plays held at Furness Abbey and was a close associate of the 1988 director, David Marcus.

In 1989 Hunter Davies was one of the jocular journalists who had at one time pilloried Barrow. His deprecating view of the town was challenged by Alice Leach and she instigated

Alice Leach

an invitation to him from Barrow in Furness Civic and Local History Society to visit the town. Naturally, she took him on a tour of Barrow that included Furness Abbey, which she regarded as the jewel in the crown of Furness. From this visit Mr Hunter had to adjust his derogatory views and the meeting ended in mutual respect.

In her later years Mrs Leach researched the Coucher Book in some detail and was able to acquire slides of the illuminated letters for the Society. She championed the Abbey to the last, attending a conference about new research on Jocelin of Furness, the hagiographer of four saints including St Patrick. She was delighted when a medieval trackway was discovered near the Abbey Mill Café in 2009 and promptly contacted the local newspaper to advertise the find. The BBC and Channel 4 interviewed her at Furness Abbey about the phenomenal discovery of an abbot with his crosier and ring in 2010. Her hope was that it would expand the profile of Furness and give it the level of prominence it deserves.

Her legacy speaks for itself in the books and research she leaves and in the lives of the people she touched and inspired. As Vanessa Allen says, *A History of Furness Abbey* gives a unique insight into the abbey's history and is a lasting legacy of its remarkable author." Her ex-pupil Kay Thornton adds, "I will always remember her with fond regard as she was my teacher but also my mentor and friend." A spokesperson from Furness Abbey Fellowship said, "Alice Leach was keen to bring the Abbey to the forefront again after many years in the doldrums and was involved in the early discussions and set up of Furness Abbey Fellowship. She will be missed but her legacy through her scholarship and work will remain and she will continue to inspire."

CHAPTER 27

DARON DEIGHTON
Mason - 2021

Daron Deighton

Daron works for English Heritage as a stone mason and oversaw the project to conserve and repair parts of Furness Abbey which were most at risk. This work went on for some months during 2020 and 2021, completing in May. The work was undertaken during Covid restrictions and the plans to have "Conservation in Action" was abandoned. However, once these were reduced, staff and members of Furness Abbey Fellowship were permitted access to see the amazing work close up. Scaffolding surrounded the abbey for months and it caused a lot of discussion in the local community. The extracts below are taken from a discussion with Daron at the end of the work, on a sunny day looking out over the abbey.

25 May 2021 Furness Abbey

Q: What made you become a mason?

Daron: I like history and stonemasonry. I started as a brick layer and found it boring. The company I worked for did more stonework and that's when I got into doing more stonework. I joined English Heritage in 1988 and have never looked back.

Q: Your love of history makes the connection to the masons of the past. How do you think your job differs now?

Daron: Not a lot, obviously now we use electric grinders and things like that, but we still use traditional methods and what they used to use. Similar tools: hammers, chisels though we use tungsten tipped. They used to use just metal which would have been sharpened on site - there would have been workshops with blacksmiths working on site.

Q: That's interesting, so there must have been a place for them to stay on site would you say?

Daron: Definitely, in all the abbeys I've worked on there would have been blacksmiths always making stuff, all the chisels-sharpening them and that.

Q: What innovations and improvements have you seen in the job in comparison to the old masons' experience?

Daron: I have a lot of respect for them. We have tungsten tips, more mechanical tools, in those days it was all done by hand, even the saws. Compared to then it's a lot easier now. We use mechanical tools when we can if we are allowed.

Q: So, when can't you use power tools?

Daron: On pointing, open joints-it can cause damage, it depends on the building and the age and whether the architect will let you. English Heritage won't usually let you, that's their policy. You can slip and mark the stone, maybe spoil building and masonry that's been there for years.

Q: Is Furness Abbey one of your favourites? Be careful how you answer this! (laughs)

Daron: Yes. It's a nice abbey. It's a very nice abbey. A lot of the abbeys I've worked on are different stone, all yellow stone. This is red sandstone so it's different. Nice stone.

Q: Is it soft to work with?

Daron: No, it's hard. I know it's worn but when Dave's (the other mason) been cutting it, or I've been cutting, it it's very hard. Tough stone really.

Q: Would you say that this stone is softer than St Bees sandstone further up the coast?

Daron: It's hard to say. If this has stood for nearly 1000 years you don't know how long it will last or how it will wear. Each stone, everywhere you go-one side could be pristine, but the other corner might be worn because of the wind, you just don't know with the rain and everything. Just wears!

Q: Which parts of the job have you enjoyed during this piece of work, and which are you proudest of?

Daron: It's all been very good. It's been very wet and cold some of the time, but we've had good lads working as a good team. It's been very enjoyable, and we got the job done well and worked as a team.

Q: Have you ever found anything interesting?

Daron: Not really, have worked on loads of Roman and medieval stuff. We used to have to have to draw things, you know, carvings and that. We used to take photos and get them developed at Boots but now it's all digital, a huge change!

Q: Which is the most iconic part?

Daron: The arches. There are a lot of steel bars in there. One arch fell down while we were working on it, so we had to repair that too. The work to repair it previously wasn't that good. It had been poorly repaired. We have repaired it properly now.

Q: Oh really? Do you think this would be from the restoration work in the 1930s.

Daron: No more modern, you follow instructions and architect's directives, sometimes the ideas change, and things don't work out.

Q: Would you recommend the job to young people now?

Daron: Yes. But it's hard to engage them because of the money. We used to show people what we did in open days. Lots of interest. The first question they always asked was how much money can you make? They can probably make more as a bricklayer. It's a great trade but the money isn't great. And there are different types of masons, specialisms. Dave (the other mason) who worked at Canterbury Cathedral - wants to make everything flush, but you can't do that here; you've got to go with what you've got. It costs £30,000 to train at York College, but guys do it and then they leave because of the earnings.

Q: That's sad then, isn't it? Can you think of why they might want to stay?

Daron: Well, we are lucky working for English Heritage. You get to see things you wouldn't usually see, like the presbytery and bell tower here. Nobody's going to see what we have seen unless we put some goats up there to trim the grass. (chuckles)

Q: What is your next project?

Daron: Next project? Richmond Castle, so close to home and no lodging. Then there is talk of Rievaulx, Whitby and Scarborough Castle. All local to me.

Q: Well, I'm glad you enjoyed working here, perhaps we will see you again? Thanks for your time today.

Daron: Probably at some time. It's been enjoyable.

CHAPTER 28

LUCY RONALD
Site Manager - 2021

I have always lived locally. When I was very small my grandma lived on Hawcoat Lane and my mum would always drive past the Abbey on our way from Gleaston. The ruins left a big impression on me, but at the time I did not realise how big.

Later, when I left university I wanted to work in a museum. I got a volunteer placement with Lakeland Arts Trust - working at Abbot Hall, Blackwell and Museum of Lakeland Life and Industry. This led to a paid job at Stott Park Bobbin Mill (an EH site but managed by Lakeland Arts Trust at that time).

Then a Site Supervisor post came up at Furness Abbey in 2005 (when Brenda Thompson retired). I applied for it, and I actually got it! Believe it or not, I intended it to be temporary!

Initially I job shared with another girl (Hayley Thomson) and the area manager (actually called the Visitor Operations Manager - abbreviated to VOM) was called Andrew Dunning and he was based out of Furness Abbey.

I really threw myself into the job, there was a lot to do. EH was in process of becoming a more commercial operation. It sounds like a cliché, but really no two days at the abbey are the same - apart from the relentless tasks like toilet cleaning!

A day at the abbey starts with a site check. This is always a privilege - even in horizontal rain! Unfortunately, it is also the point in the day when we discover what people have been up to on site overnight. I once arrived to find the Abbot's House had been completely bound up in a tangle of extremely heavy duty blue rope! Goodness knows why it was done. From the moment the doors open at 10am our working day is defined by the visitors. On a busy day we can be talking non-stop for several hours. There have been many interesting characters and regular visitors over the years!

A quieter day provides an opportunity to catch up with admin (there's no shortage of this), plus cleaning and retail tasks.

When the crack appeared in the presbytery wall in 2007, this had quite an impact on my working life and continues to do so!

There were several years of archaeological investigation, three years of disruptive repair works, seven years of monitoring and then the conservation works in 2020/21 have all added interest to my working day! There have been lots of contractors on site, project meetings, and endless sections of heras fencing to pick up (either blown over in the wind or knocked down by trespassers, who knows). But the work was essential and the end result definitely worth the trouble. Then, in 2011, the site supervisor role was replaced and I got the role of Site Manager. This new role naturally came with a lot of new responsibilities but I threw myself in to it all.

Initially (in 2012 when it was formed) I was a bit wary of Furness Abbey Fellowship! I had returned from maternity leave, straight into the new role of site manager and was introduced to the group! I wondered who they were, what they wanted and how they would impact on my work. But I feel that over time we have developed a good working relationship and now I feel we are extremely lucky to have as supportive and proactive a group as FAF on our side. 2014 brought the crozier back to Furness on permanent display (thank you FAF) and a surge in visitor numbers as a result. Then, of course, there's all the fun of the (Medieval) fair!

As for the future, the museum and the interpretation out on site both need a refresh. I would like the abbey grounds to be more accessible. In fact there are relatively simple interventions that could open up some new areas. Overall I want visitors to have a great experience from start to finish, and go home to tell all their friends!

AFTERWORD

GILL JEPSON
Author and Local Historian-2021

The original idea for this book was suggested by Ron, my co-writer and abbey enthusiast. He joined Furness Abbey Fellowship some years ago and has proved to be innovative and keen ever since. We are always looking at ways to extend our love and knowledge of Furness Abbey to others and to encourage people to support and visit it. This book is just one method we have used.

I found the idea of telling the abbey's story through the people who lived here, or were connected to it in some way, irresistible and, despite having numerous other writing projects on the go, I felt inspired to begin at once. We have tried to cover the many eras and include as many of the personalities who are key in the abbey's story. Each character has been researched or where there is no specific person we have created a fictional character to fulfil the role; for example the Medieval Mason. We know no names, but we have researched how they lived and worked and obviously have the evidence of their creativity in the abbey itself. It was particularly exciting to be able to bring some stories up to date, as with the modern mason. We were lucky enough to witness a huge programme of conservation being undertaken by English Heritage and were able to not only speak with, but have a tour of the work by the mason and architect. The comparisons were amazing and hopefully we have gained another story which no doubt will be on-going.

My connection and love of Furness Abbey goes back to my childhood. Being local I was very familiar with the ruins; it was our Sunday walk, school trip and place to be. I remember when the only entrance was the Custodian's ticket booth and when the abbey was perhaps more finely tuned in terms of paths and grass.

Later after returning to the area in the 1980s, a brand new (if somewhat hideous) visitor centre was built after the Department for the Environment morphed into English Heritage.

The intervening years allowed me to introduce the next generation to the abbey and we visited often, completing school projects or joining in with various activities here. I regularly brought children from my class to visit - either for projects or just for fun, from nursery through to primary age. This carried on with grandchildren and the intimacy grew as one of my sons worked around and in the abbey as an archaeologist in 2009-10, during the period in which the abbot and crosier was discovered in the presbytery. This was followed up with a Channel 4 News report produced by my other son, which showcased the find and the abbey nationally. By now the abbey was becoming a family affair in more ways than one.

I began writing about the abbey in my children's fantasy novels, *Out of Time*, and with the success of these, visited schools and interest groups to give talks or provide workshops. Inevitably, the contact with schools has led to me to provide tours of the abbey as well. Since 2011 I have written numerous local history books and have always included Furness Abbey to allow people a taster of the place. In 2022 a specific nostalgia book, *Furness Abbey through Time*, commissioned by Amberley Books, will appear. I am excited to do this and it will accompany my own history of the abbey later in the year.

It was around 2011 that I had the idea for the Fellowship and to offer support to English Heritage to put the abbey truly on the map. I had recently met Alice Leach, a well know local historian and advocate of the abbey. We discussed the low profile the abbey seemed to have at lunch during a history conference about Jocelin of Furness. We decided to keep in touch and very soon had planned to contact English Heritage to discover what prospects there were for the abbey in the future. We had heard through the grapevine that a remarkable discovery of an abbot had been made and we wanted to know what would happen to the artefacts. We met with Richard Polley of English Heritage and expressed our concerns and he divulged that the abbey had only 4,500 visitors at that time. We were heartened to hear that an announcement would soon be made.

By 2012 I had contacted numerous people with a great passion for the abbey. One person was Stuart Appleby who was about to launch a living history group had made a promotional film for me. We discussed the possibility of forming a "friends" group. We knew that Alice had previously formed one, but it had not lasted awfully long: this did not deter us. A few others joined in the discussion, and we all met at the Red Lion at Dalton: an eclectic group of re-enactors, artists, historians, writers, and abbey enthusiasts. Around the time that we formed the group, Channel 4 News sent a crew to film the abbot's crosier and ring with English Heritage. Patrick Corbett, one of our members and local artist, spoke about how much potential the abbey had.

We didn't formalise as a small charity until 2012 and by then we had begun discussions with Clea Warner from English Heritage. Things moved on rapidly; sadly Alice Leach became ill and could not continue, but we kept in touch through Vanessa Allen who was a member of Barrow Civic Society of which Alice was Chair. We developed an excellent working relationship with EH and before we knew it, we were fundraising for a cabinet for the crosier to be displayed in. We had our first Medieval Fair in 2013 and although we were not sure it would be a success we were gratified by the attendance. We were astounded at the hundreds of people who came throughout the day, and we knew that the fair would become a regular event.

From this we discovered the love of the abbey is widespread across the community and there was an appetite for it to be a centre for heritage activities and education. Furness Abbey Fellowship have since developed the annual medieval fair and other smaller events through the year; Iron Shepherds, a living history group have been integral to this and are the lynch pin to these activities. Our first fair cost £700 to put on but as it has grown it now costs about £3,500. We fundraise and are self-sustaining and hopefully EH benefit too.

We constantly try to reach a wider audience and unexpectedly in 2019 Dan Snow, the TV Historian, came to Barrow for a show. I cheekily tweeted him and offered a tour of the abbey. To my surprise he accepted, and as we walked around a deserted abbey, he said he was astounded that he had never heard of it. We garnered extensive publicity for the abbey from this and Dan even mentioned the abbey in his lecture later.

So, have we helped to make an impact? I think so. We are always keen to improve and extend the prominence of Furness and we have a healthy working relationship with English Heritage (which is now a charity). We have instigated numerous fundraisers, including the crosier case. More recently we reached our target to buy some locational plaques for the abbey. These are to add to the interest and will be useful until interpretation signs are replaced. We have in some way assisted with increasing visitor numbers, but the real boost was the crosier of course. We hope that the visitor numbers will continue to increase. Obviously, there is always more work to do, but for now the future of the building is more secure.

At the time of writing, we hope once the amazing tranche of conservation is complete that the abbey can become a more significant visitor attraction than ever. Certainly, our seventh Medieval Fair in September 2021 and we continue planning for the next. And we have many other ideas in the pipeline. We know that English Heritage have invested a lot of time and money into this very important abbey and the least we can do is to encourage more visitors and shout out what a wonderful place this is.

We look forward to extending the story of Furness Abbey over the coming years and recording what happens in the future. Above all we want people to love the abbey as much as we do and contribute to its well-being and extend its life for future generations to enjoy.

Gill Jepson

ACKNOWLEDGEMENTS

Although our stories have imagined elements with invented dialogue, we have tried to make the events as accurate as possible. The completion of this book owes much to those people who contributed their memories and stories and sometimes photographs.

Thanks to the following people for their help and contributions:

- *Emily Smith, for the photograph of her great grandfather Thomas Shaw and recollections of his work in conserving Furness Abbey.*
- *Vanessa Allen, Chair of Barrow Civic Society, for memories and photograph of Alice Leach, their founder.*
- *Daron Deighton, Mason for agreeing to an interview and photograph.*
- *Nathaniel Jepson, ex-Field Archaeologist, for contribution and photograph permission.*
- *Lucy Ronald, Site Manager of Furness Abbey, for interview and photograph permission.*
- *Leeann Herbert, Secretary and Trustee of Furness Abbey Fellowship, for contribution and photo permission.*
- *Liz Critchley, Treasurer and Trustee of Furness Abbey Fellowship, for contribution and photograph permission.*
- *Walter Johnson & John Twyford for memories and anecdotes about the Mystery Plays.*
- *Susan Benson, Cumbria Archive Service*
- *Various people who shared their thoughts about the abbey in Facebook posts etc.*

In addition, we must thank the following local companies who have generously contributed to the cost of producing the book; we are extremely grateful.

We also received a grant through Barra Culture: more thanks

BIBLIOGRAPHY

- *Antiquities of Furness* Father Thomas West
- *Annales Furnesienses* Thomas Alcock Beck
- *Barrow and District* E Barnes
- *Jocelin of Furness* Edited by Clare Downham
- *Furness Abbey* Alice Leach
- *A Handy Guide to the Ruins of Furness Abbey* JP Morris
- *Furness and Furness Abbey* Francis Evans
- *A Sketch of Furness and Cartmel* Charles M Jopling
- *Furness Abbey and its Neighbourhood* James Payn
- *Furness Abbey Guidebook* English Heritage
- *Furness Past and Present* Joseph Richardson
- *Furness Abbey: Romance, Scholarship and Culture* C Dade Robertson

Lightning Source UK Ltd.
Milton Keynes UK
UKHW050326130822
407229UK00003B/67